Healing the wounds of medicine

STORIES AND JOURNALING FOR PHYSICIANS

shineMD

MARIA C.COLON-GONZALEZ, MD

Disclaimer: Details of the characters in the stories have been changed to protect their identity.

To request permissions, contact the publisher at mcgmed2010@gmail.com.
Paperback: 979-8-218-09999-2
Ebook: 979-8-218-10000-1
Cover and Illustration Art by Sherri Marteney

Printed and Created by shineMD
Email: shineMD@gmail.com
Facebook: MDwrite2heal
Instagram: MDwrite2heal

Table of Contents

Welcome

Before we begin, let me introduce myself. I've been a physician since 2010, graduating from the University of Puerto Rico. I am a holistic lifestyle and family physician. I practice in Texas, where I work with a diversity of patients and colleagues. I love my work and couldn't imagine doing anything else. But there have been times, many times, when I've come home howling, wondering why I ever went into a profession that has treated me so badly time and time again. I have discovered just how hard it is to work and to heal people, in a medical system that puts profits over people, dehumanizes its physicians, and subjects us to working conditions that veer from brutal to abusive. The call, "Physician heal thyself," has never been more timely. We need to heal ourselves if we are to heal our patients, but more importantly, we need to transform ourselves if we are to continue to practice medicine and regain our passion for patient care.

We have all suffered from trauma. Trauma stops us in our tracks, freezing our bodies, thought processes, and capacity to navigate our emotions. Yet, for some, trauma hides like an insidious tumor, devouring its host unseen and in silence. Physicians are exposed to primary and secondary trauma daily. We struggle to make it through another day of treating patients, watching them die, mending horrific wounds, while we hope to make the best decisions for people we often never see again.

And as I've confronted the trauma and pathologies inherent in our profession, I've realized I am not alone in feeling drained and battered by my work. I am not the only physician who has been put down, sabotaged, and screamed at by colleagues, supervisors, and patients. Every one of us has suffered for our work, even though it's work we love. As I came to realize how prevalent this abuse was, I realized that we physicians need healing as much as we need to heal. Our work has, in many ways, traumatized us, and it's done so through an insidious process of dehumanizing both physicians and patients. Fortunately, through healing and metamorphosis, we can experience the power of Post-Traumatic Growth. Post-Traumatic Growth is a way to live that moves us toward a life of harmony and authenticity.

Having worked through my own trauma due to my profession, I have discovered a pathway forward that is uniquely designed for physicians who feel alone in their suffering. Silenced by our own guilt, lest we dare complain about a profession that pays so well and gives us such high status—the trauma we take home is buried as if it didn't matter.

Overwhelmed by our fears and doubts and confusion, the abuse inflicted upon us has become normalized. We need an outlet for our own trauma if we are to heal others. And while we can be there for others, to be truly effective we must focus on our own healing and self-care. By doing the healing work in these pages, your gift as a healer will become stronger. So let this journal be your outlet, as you take the first step toward healing yourself.

Why Journaling

I've written this guided journal to help you address safety, attune to your body, accept your emotions, and empower you to feel more empathy, not just for others, but for yourself. Rather than exercises, I want you to think of each question or suggestion as "contemplation"—not something for you to do, but something for you to think about, as you record your thoughts in the pages of this journal, free of judgment, free of scrutiny. In these contemplations you'll work on, I've drawn on principles of narrative therapy combined with creativity and embodied practice, to help you heal yourself. You'll discover that if you feel you struggle with burnout or compassion fatigue, feel the system is exploiting and abusing you, and feel powerless over the moral injury, these healing contemplations are for you.

The guided journaling exercises that follow will help you own your stories. It is in owing and honoring the good and bad of their stories that we can transform and heal. My aim is to help doctors avoid the victim mentality that some feel or the sense of being stuck doing work that doesn't resemble the career you may have wanted. The victim mentality tells us that bad things have happened to us and will continue to happen. Others have brought on this state of affairs and there's nothing we can do to change if—change will only invite more problems, and probably fail. With this view, there is no point in trying, and there is no growth. The same thinking can keep us stuck, even if we don't feel victimized. If we feel stuck, we fear that any effort to become unstuck will only sink us deeper into the rut of our career. But these perceptions are distortions of the world we live and work in. They focus on the problematic issues we contend with while failing to acknowledge our agency—our ability to create positive change and to define our own lives. Guided journaling empowers you to tap into your inner power, and grow into the confident, grounded healer you set out to become when you first envisioned yourself as a doctor.

Through this journal, you can explore your own Post-Traumatic Growth as you identify the ways our profession wounds us both directly and indirectly. Through journaling, you will experience self-grace and self-compassion which in turn will improve your physician-patient relationships. By inviting you to explore your curiosity and humility, you will discover tools to facilitate your own healing, as you reflect on the enriching experience of healing others.

But if you're a busy doctor you're probably thinking that writing in a journal is just not going to happen. You have a million things to get done each day, and by the time you have a moment to sit down, you don't have the energy to write a grocery list, much less your inner thoughts and feelings. Besides, you might be thinking, how can a simple journal help heal the wounds inflicted by the medical profession? The things you've been through just today alone could fill your journal, and your pain is so deep and raw and hidden that there's just no fixing it.

Maybe a journal won't erase the trauma, but I want you to know that thinking through the questions, insights, and stories that follow will help you to heal. Healing is a process, not an instant fix, and through the process of healing, you will come to see your work as a physician in a new light, one that makes the traumas to come more endurable, the ones that have passed more tender and distant. With time, those wounds will be transformed, and in their place will come an inner strength as you reclaim the joy, confidence, and security that trauma stole from you. You will discover that by practicing the rhythm of slowing down through journaling and quieting your thinking mind, you will create more space for compassion and confidence. You will gain a new power to help you navigate the challenges of medicine. And you will gain new energies to make juggling all the demands of medicine, caring for your family and home, and enjoying a social life not only possible but less stressful. When we lay bare our truths through our writing, we become protagonists in our lives, rather than victims of circumstances beyond our control. Let me take you there, to that place inside your heart, where that protagonist dwells hidden and alone. Let me open the door wide and welcome you to the space where your healing will begin.

***

I can shake off everything as I write; my sorrows disappear, my courage is reborn.

Anne Frank.

***

Investing in Yourself

Time is a luxury, especially for physicians. Journaling also takes time and requires setting aside some time each day, time you just don't have. But that time is yours. The time you set aside for journaling is time you set aside for *you*. There's no one else you have to answer to, no one else you have to serve. It's your time. And it's an investment that will give you a guaranteed return. With time, your journaling will enable you to reap the fruits of healing and inspire you to new heights as your stress and traumatic experiences fade away.

Journaling to Power Your Brain and Body

If there's one thing physicians understand, it's the human body. By using this journal to begin your healing journey, you will discover that the act of journaling is not just about moving a pen across a page. Writing—real, pen-in-hand cursive writing—activates both hemispheres of the brain, creating and interpreting patterns, while integrating data from our experiences with our feelings and emotions. The left side of the brain is responsible for our rational and analytical thinking, and the right side of the brain—the part of our brain we too often neglect in medicine—is where our creative, emotional, and intuitive Self dwells. As the left side of our brain becomes occupied with the act of writing, the right side of our brain is busy accessing our emotions and intuition. This cognitive and emotional duality fosters a creative and beautiful healing.

Journaling also helps us to face our daily challenges and concerns, reach our goals, modify our daily routines, recognize our triggers and how to best manage them, and identify and embrace our emotions. As physicians, we have been trained to subordinate our emotions to our logic, quash our subjectivity in favor of objectivity, and deny the traumas of our profession. But by suppressing stress and trauma, we risk developing cognitive and mental health problems, becoming chronically fatigued, and compromising our immune system, leading to physical illnesses. Journaling helps us gain clarity, self-awareness, and confidence, qualities that give meaning to our lives and help reduce body tension, eliminate negative thoughts, and restore our focus.

The Unspoken Traumas of Our Profession

"But I'm not traumatized," you might insist. "I love my job, it's so rewarding!" Yes, being a physician is immensely rewarding. We heal, we save lives, we work in the world of science, and we interact with dozens of people each day from all walks of life. But that doesn't mean our profession comes without cost. From our education in medical schools which beat us into submission, excluded women, people of color, older students, trans and gay students, disabled students, questioning students, and first-generation students, to residencies and internships which kept us sleep-deprived, insulted by our superiors and often by our patients, and taught us that the slightest mistake could have profound and life-changing consequences to our patients and our careers, we entered our professions as M.D.'s already beaten down, already scarred with parts of our Selves diminished. By the time we'd graduated and finished our residencies, we barely recognized our daily trauma.

And yet, trauma has defined our work. We tell our patients they or their loved ones are dying. Or that they must have parts of themselves cut out. Or that they will never walk again, or speak again, or that the baby they are carrying will be stillborn or born with a serious health problem. We tell our patients that their hearts must be replaced. Or their lungs. Or their kidneys. We desperately try to stop their bleeding when they've been torn apart in a car accident, or been stabbed, or shot. We watch them die. We tell parents their children have died, or children their parents have died. And sometimes we never even see them, the patients whose x-rays we examine, noting the tumors that will kill them, or the blood that reveals deadly sickle-cells or leukemia cells that we know courses through someone's veins. Or the slice of tissue that is riddled with cancer cells, the chart a colleague has asked us to review that shows a pattern of symptoms we recognize as a rare but cruel disease.

Our traumas are not always about our patients. Often, they are inflicted on us by our colleagues or our superiors. The competition that transforms any success into an invitation for a battle. The colleagues who lie about us, spreading insidious but powerful rumors that shape how others see us. The colleagues who question our medical orders and treatments. The colleagues who sabotage us, at first in small ways, over time in bigger ways. The superiors who insult us, mock us, give us impossible orders or overlook us in favor of their favorites. The accusations of misconduct or malpractice, the internal or medical board investigations, and threats of ruin that haunt many, all too often for no better reason than someone felt threatened by our competence or pounced the minute they saw we'd slipped. Or in retaliation for our putting patient safety first and challenging a colleague or superior. We learn early on to get through each day as if working in a field of landmines, stepping carefully with every interaction, while we try to do our jobs.

And then we go home. For some of us, going home means even more work—60 to 90 minutes of work at home is the average! The kids to pick up, feed, help with homework, bathe, and get to bed. The spouse to placate or please, the house to clean, the friends to catch up on (if we've any friends left because we're so busy we don't have time for them), and then, when all is done, the work we brought home, the patients to call, the paperwork to fill out. For others, the lucky ones, home is a respite from the stress of work, where we're met with loving, supportive partners. Yet how many times have we come home and vented about the patients who screamed at us, the tragic life we lost, the colleague who undermined us, the supervising physician who punished us for some imagined offense? How often have you been so tired you could barely understand a word your partner uttered, as s/he tried to share their own horrific or wondrous day with you? How often have you just wanted to run away to the beach and forget about it all, just curl up with a good book and a stiff drink and declare yourself retired?

And then the friends who tell you what a great job you have, how lucky you are to make such good money (never mind the loans you took out for med school that you'll be repaying all your life), and how much fun it must be to have such cool work saving people's lives. And you resist the urge to tell them you'd give anything to drive a school bus filled with screaming, fighting kids because it would be much easier. Instead, you just smile and nod and change the subject, thinking you sure don't want your kids going into medicine. You want them to have a life. And you want one, as well.

The truth is, if you are a practicing physician, you live with trauma, both primary and secondary, every day. Not a day goes by that you don't face some sort of existential pain or human suffering that you have learned to bury. Sometimes it's someone else's trauma, one where you've been given a front seat as witness, if not director. Sometimes it's your colleague's, as you've watched from the sidelines, afraid to be drawn closer. Sometimes it's the colleague who has taken their own life, and you think, will I be next? And sometimes it's your own complex trauma, and you've just stuffed it away where no one can see it, least of all you.

It's time for you to see it. It's time to acknowledge that as a physician, you live with trauma daily. I know, oh so well, that after an event that triggers a trauma response, it can be hard to unpack our feelings, thoughts, and emotions, something even harder for physicians who have been taught to keep them packed away. Yet we need to unpack our baggage before we can be rid of it—which is precisely what writing in our journals does. So, here's how to do it.

How to Use This Journal

(Without it Becoming Another Thing You Have to Do)

The good news is, when journaling, you do not need to follow any rules or structures. Journaling is not the EMR, and nobody will be reviewing your work to code and bill for it or measure your productivity. In the pages that follow, I will guide you, but *you* are the one in charge.

I have organized the journal into three parts. The first, Acknowledging Your Trauma, explores the many ways in which a medical career can traumatize and retraumatize us. Part Two, Healing Your Trauma, continues to explore the ways we are stressed and abused at work, but in this section, you'll find yourself taking steps to begin healing, little by little. Finally, in Part Three, Post-Traumatic Growth, you go even further into the healing process as you begin to emerge from the wounded past and integrate the many broken pieces of your Self that have been damaged by the stressful and brutalizing work of being a physician.

I have provided you four types of reflections or activities.

Contemplations are just that—spaces for you to contemplate questions that touch on what you need, value, desire or believe. Contemplations typically focus on present-level thoughts and involved compassionate introspection. **Reflections** are more liked meditations, they help you to open up by seeing what is being mirrored and encourage you to think about specific details related to your job, career, or life that will help you to identify ways in which the medical profession has affected you. You need both, Contemplations and Reflections, to help you to take actionable steps. **Create** calls on you to pick up a pen, pencil, crayon, or whatever you want to use, and draw freely. No one will grade or judge you—this is your space to use a different part of your brain to freely express yourself. Finally, **Step Forward** entries encourage you to think about ways you can repair the damage, change course, make progress, or reimagine your life to experience a healthier, happier life.

Write and draw freely as things come up and banish any need for perfection. Embrace your flaws! It's in our flaws and imperfections that our souls reside. What's more, in journaling, when we focus on perfection and correct our grammatical errors or rewrite something to capture better phrasing, we create roadblocks to our own healing. Try not to go there. Drive freely on the highway of your mind, brain, and emotions. And take your time. Nobody is checking if the journaling was completed in 48 hours! You have no deadlines to meet. If you need to sit with a thought or a question, reflect on it before going at it, give yourself permission to hold the tension until you can create meaning for your experience. Your journal is your personal place to store your fears, struggles, and any other emotion without judgment or punishment from the healthcare system. Journaling will help you reprocess the traumatic events of medicine and start to see goodness in your career. Journaling will craft your identity and authenticity as a physician as you become an expert on your Self, and what being a physician means to you— and to you alone.

To ensure your journaling benefits you as much as possible, without it becoming yet another thing you have to do, set aside a time, even if just 15 minutes—even ten minutes or five minutes, but 15 minutes is a good start—every day. That day might be early in the morning before anyone else in the house wakes up. It might be at the end of the day, before you even think about dinner, or the end of the night, before bed. It may even be some stolen moments in the middle of the day, during your break. **But** here's the thing—you need to schedule this time in the same way you'd schedule a patient, or your kids' soccer practice, or your yoga class, and you need to think of it not as something you need to do or want to do—but as something you get to do—because you deserve this time. This is time for you. It's sacred time, time no one else can pester you. They need to learn to respect this sacred time that's yours. Set a daily alarm on your phone to remind you, settle into your writing chair, and turn off your phone so no one can disturb you. Settle into your quiet space, where you feel safe, with a cup of tea or other favorite beverage, maybe even light a scented candle, and write to relax. Write to awaken, to create something new, or to return to your roots. Write to take care—of you.

You can journal using a black pen, or you might sometimes want to use colors representing your feelings. I recommend you keep various colored pens/pencils nearby, not for extra work, but for those moments when colors can aid in expressing what you feel. In the drawing reflections, you can choose to draw in pen and ink or use colors to express and let out all that holds you back. If you select a different color from your usual color, what does that new color mean to you? If you face a blank page, with a blank stare, what does that blank space mean to you? What thoughts or feelings are you blocking, keeping out? Which thoughts or feelings do you want to bring in? Let yourself draw and write freely, free of judgment, free of perfection, free of fear.

Grounding ourselves in our bodies and the present moment will be essential in this journey. At times, you will look for any escape from the present. You'll come home from work with your head full of worry about something disturbing that happened, or might happen, or probably will happen. Or you'll be angry, furious even, at someone who treated you badly or violated your sense of safety, or your sense of ethics. Your heart will be pounding and all you can think of is wishing you were anywhere but in the present moment.

If that happens, return to this journal, and pick an activity that helps you to become grounded. If a reflection becomes too heavy, too stressful, use your senses to take a pause and then decide if you're going to return to the contemplation, or choose another one. Don't run from your emotions, acknowledge them. Get curious about what emotions you are feeling and how these emotions are present in your body. Feel them. Are they in your shoulders? Your stomach? Your hands? Have they seeped into your legs, come to rest in your gut? Breathe deeply before you pick up your pen. Breathe long and slow. Use different tools to self-regulate and bring your body back into the experience. When you're ready, pick up your pen and begin.

PART ONE

Acknowledging Your Trauma

Dreaming It

I went into medicine because I wanted to help people live healthier lives.
I imagined myself practicing in a holistic, integrative center where people
could receive medical attention, mental health services, fitness, and nutrition
all under one roof. I wanted to treat the whole patient because doing so is
the only way to truly heal them.

It wasn't until after my residency, that I realized I'd strayed too far away from
my dream. It took years of working in an abusive system for me to realize
that not only was the work environment killing me, but it was preventing
me from growing as a physician. I needed to return to my dream and find
a position where I could be the physician, I set out to become. I am now
working on creating my own practice in the holistic setting I had envisioned

when I first entered medicine, but I'm still not there. As I pursue this dream, I continue to note the many ways in which the reality and the dream have diverged, even as I embrace working in a more fulfilling position.

Has reality cast your own dream aside? Most of us discover that the future we imagined, is not the present we now live. In many ways, that's fine—by living in the present, we discover wondrous gifts. But in other ways, losing sight of our dreams takes us away from our best lives. The twists and turns of life can take us to unexpected destinies, but they can also take us from our chosen paths. Whatever your own dream, your medical career has undoubtedly come with some unexpected twists and turns. Let's explore those twists and turns.

Reflection: Think back to the doctor you wanted to be, even before starting medical school. Describe how you had envisioned yourself as a doctor. What kind of medicine did you dream of practicing? How did you envision your patients, colleagues, and friends viewing you? What did you imagine you would spend your day doing?

_____

_____

_____

_____

_____

_____

_____

_____

Reflection: What was your motivation for becoming a doctor? Why did you choose your profession?

_____

_____

_____

_____

_____

_____

_____

Contemplation: Have you become that doctor? If so, in what ways have you met or exceeded your dreams? If not, what has changed? In what ways have you drifted from your dream? Has this drift been toward a better dream, or away from a dream you still cherish?

_____

_____

_____

_____

_____

_____

_____

Reflection: Do those qualities of the profession that drew you to medicine still exist? In what ways has medicine changed?

_____

_____

_____

_____

_____

_____

_____

Step Forward: Are there ways you can bring those lost qualities back into your career?

_____

_____

_____

_____

_____

_____

_____

_____

Step Forward: If you have not yet become the doctor you once envisioned you'd become or the one you still hope to become, what do you need to do to be more faithful to yourself and be that doctor? If you have become that doctor, what did you do that made it possible?

_____

_____

_____

_____

_____

_____

_____

_____

_____

_____

Naming It

You've dreamed of becoming a doctor—a certain kind of doctor. And even if you have become the kind of doctor you'd envisioned, that dream has not come without a cost. To understand what sacrificing or achieving that dream has cost, you must understand that there's a name for what you've been through. That name is: Abuse. Acknowledging you've been abused doesn't mean you're a victim, and it doesn't mean you don't have a respectable profession, one you may even love. But you have paid your dues to get there. No matter how brilliant a physician you are, no matter how successful, I have no doubt that if you look objectively at the process of becoming a doctor, you'll recognize the abuse.

Our first immersion in the culture that molds us into the doctors we become begins in medical school. Medical school is our family of origin. Those first few years have a significant impact on our identity as physicians which isn't always healthy. Medical school is where we learn to compete as we never have before and where we learn to sacrifice our sleep, our families, our friends, and all our other interests, as we study round the clock. This education can leave a long trail of dysfunction that is reflected in how you relate to your patients, colleagues, and others. But by exploring this abuse, you can, dear physician, heal thyself!

***

Anna is a 40-year-old successful physician but still becomes upset thinking of her medical school experience years before.

I had prepared well for the anatomy exam. "Ladies," the professor began, "luck is important in life so to be fair; I've put all the possible questions in these vases. All you need to do is pick one from each vase and answer it as we go. If you get the difficult ones, I'm not to blame, it's your luck." It was my lucky day! Time after time I picked the easy questions. But guess what? The moment someone had a difficult one they couldn't answer, the teacher would come back and ask me because, he explained, "I was too lucky." Over almost two hours, I had answered far more questions than anyone else. And then the professor looked at me and said, "You can get out. You passed the exam, and you have clearly studied enough to get above 8/10 in the exam. Your performance today was way above 7/10. But I'll give you a barely passing 5 because your face shows anxiety, and I don't like that at all." It took me a moment to realize what I had heard. The other students were in shock too. Everyone was looking at me, but I was frozen and could not speak.

I said a "thank you," trying to swallow my tears and humiliation. I felt exhausted, relieved, angry, sad, humiliated, helpless, and ready to explode! All these emotions flooded me all at once. I was sure I was getting a 9/10, but instead, I walked out of that room with a 5/10 based on how I looked and the emotion I was reflecting. But what could I do? I felt powerless over his cruel abuse. I said nothing and to this day, I regret it. I felt as if I'd been bullied and abused. And after that experience, my fear of oral exams increased exponentially.

***

Reflection: Were you ever humiliated as a medical student or as a resident physician? If so, can you remember what happened, including your response? (In this contemplation, just describe the act(s) and event(s), not the emotions.)

_____

_____

_____

_____

_____

_____

_____

_____

Contemplation: How did this event make you feel? Did it change the way you interacted with your colleagues? In what way?

_____

_____

_____

_____

_____

_____

_____

Contemplation: Did the experience change the way you viewed yourself professionally, or others viewed you? In what ways? Were those perceptions accurate? Why or why not?

_____

_____

_____

_____

_____

_____

_____

By the time you've graduated from medical school and made it through your residency, the weight on your shoulders has started to accumulate. Whether spoken or not, your body, mind, and soul carry the damage. All those sleepless nights studying and responding to emergencies. The highs and lows of adrenaline because we work with life and death. The anger or confusion toward administrators and health insurance companies as they become your most significant obstacle to taking care of your patients. And the patients you're caring for have love-hate relationships with you because the bill comes under your name and the wait time to see you appears to be due to your own tardiness. They don't understand that you're rushing to meet the demands of your employer and insurance companies that you see X number of patients in a day, spend as little time with them as possible, and limit your care to the least cost. If you're a woman, or a physician of color, or speak with an accent, or in some noticeable way look "different," there's not a day that you don't encounter a patient who lets you know they want another doctor, that you can't possibly be as skilled or knowledgeable as a "real" doctor. Or they think you're the nurse or the orderly, or anyone but their attending physician.

And then there is the internet and the drug commercials. They've Googled their symptoms and they know better than you what their problem is and how to treat it. They know the medicine they want because they saw a commercial on TV. Or they just want you to prescribe them something, anything because if they don't leave with a prescription, they don't think you've done your job. They may report you to the office manager, who will tell you to give the patient an injection or prescribe the requested medicine, because "the customer is always right." So much for your medical education. You feel bullied into prescribing what they request, and threatened with being written up by your manager, or even a lawsuit, if you do not comply, so you write a prescription even if you think the medication isn't necessary, could even cause adverse side effects, but it's the only way to please your patient. And then you think about the patients who need medicine but cannot afford it, and hope they filled the prescriptions you gave them, but you know many won't.

You go home each night wishing you could quit and find a new job that would be better, then you realize you are trapped with few choices due to those damn noncompete clauses that prevent you from going to a new hospital, a new clinic, a new practice. The unrelenting pressure and abuse are so damaging, traumatic even. And that trauma, abuse, and daily exploitation slowly kills the reason you became a doctor.

Contemplation: To begin your healing, you must first give a name to your pathology. Thinking back to your medical education and career as a doctor, what would you diagnose your wounds to be? You might want to call it abuse, trauma, or something more nuanced and complex. What name best fits the wounds you've suffered?

_____

_____

_____

_____

_____

_____

_____

_____

Step Forward: Describe the treatment you deserve from your patients, your colleagues, your staff, your managers, and your employers. What does it feel like to be treated less abusively? What does it look like—how do they respond when you disagree? When you say no? When you make a mistake?

How are conflicts and differences handled more humanely and kindly? How does this treatment affect your work as a physician?

_____

_____

_____

_____

_____

_____

_____

_____

_____

_____

Dr. Maria's Lessons on Unsafe Work Environments and Company

- Colleagues do not have self-boundaries and do not respect yours.
- Your contract is not clear about call duty.
- Your contract has non-compete clauses.
- You do not have administrative time to complete tasks other than seeing patients.
- Visible exclusion and subordination of people of color and women.
- The culture is about title, control, and power.
- When you deal with a disrespectful patient, management ignores you as they do not want to lose clients or profits.
- You have very little time and energy for your loved ones since the EMR follows you home.
- Self-care is not part of the work schedule.
- Leaders retaliate and marginalize you when you use your voice.
- Bureaucracy rules every decision; there are too many rules and policies.

- Passive aggressiveness or frank aggressiveness among colleagues.
- You have no say in mid-level supervision because the company sees them as equal, provides them the same CME allowances, and pays them more than half of your salary.
- You cannot express your feelings about a difficult patient to managers without being judged about your feelings.
- The profit comes before people's health.
- You are not the only one leaving; turnover is high.
- You are expected to only be a follower, and you have no voice in the business decisions that will affect your work and life.
- Your contract mentions either too much productivity via patient volume or RVUs or does not mention it at all.
- After an incident of exposure and contamination with human body fluids, you are expected to work until the end of your shift, and there is no space or time to debrief or talk about your fears.

Contemplation: Can you think of some warning signs of unhealthy work environments in medicine?

_____

_____

_____

_____

_____

_____

_____

_____

Bullying, Mobbing, and Abuse

Sometimes the abuse we suffer is so extreme, it's bullying. It's common to be bullied in the workplace, and physicians are no exception. We can be bullied by our patients, our administrators, our colleagues, even our nursing staff. And if you aren't being bullied yourself, chances are you've witnessed someone being bullied and felt powerless to intervene.

Unfortunately, bullying is contagious. Others often join in on the abuse, especially if the bullying is sanctioned by administration (which often happens when a physician has raised concerns about workplace issues or filed a complaint). When bullying extends beyond a few people engaging in the abuse, to an increasingly wider network of abusers, it's called mobbing. Mobbing doesn't get better; it generally gets worse. If you are being mobbed, it usually means you've crossed someone in administration. Your every move will be watched, your medical decisions second-guessed, and your colleagues urged to report anything you do that displeases them. It's a devastating experience, and in most cases means it's time to find a new job—which may be easier said than done.

The traumatic feeling of rejection can lead to isolation. You feel alone in the world as if nobody else has gone thru such pain. You may keep your story to yourself and with it any possibilities of healing. Or you may try to raise awareness about what is happening, only to have your efforts backfire as you become painted as a troublemaker, a liar, and a bad doctor. But the reality is, as medicine evolves and diversity increases, more and more physicians are at risk of being bullied and mobbed, and the experience is especially common to anyone who differs from the norm—the physician of color, the woman, the gay physician, or even the physician who prioritizes his or her patients over profits. Anything that makes you stand out, can make you a target in certain contexts.

As a young female physician, one of my first encounters with abuse was a violent one. I was practicing at a university and had attended a faculty luncheon one afternoon where we had many issues to discuss, including the behavior of one of my older male colleagues, Tom, and how it affected the physician-patient relationship and our residents' physician. Tom had many public outbursts when getting mad in the past. He was known for losing his temper and becoming very vocal about it. Everyone in the residency program knew when Tom was angry. The faculty team was concerned about his behavior. As we carefully approached Tom, he again lost his temper. I bluntly told him that his behavior was not appropriate. When confronted with the problem, he did not recognize the consequences and difficulties his behavior had created for the inpatient team. Before anyone could respond, he broke the plastic utensils he was using to eat his lunch and then hit the table while screaming and yelling at all his colleagues. I was shocked. I'd never seen anyone act so violently and defensively in a professional setting until that day. This old male physician could not receive feedback from his younger colleagues.

As his aggression escalated, all the other faculty members fell silent, except me. When he screamed at me, I used my voice. I informed Tom he did not have permission to use his aggression and intimidation against me, even if the other faculty members accepted his behavior. I reported his abuse to academic affairs, but little was done to correct his behavior, much less to protect me. Weeks later, Tom retaliated against me. He made false accusations against my persona, reporting me to the medical board for damning—but entirely fictional—wrongdoing. Before I could blink my eyes, this abusive colleague betrayed me and tried to build a case against me that jeopardized my medical license. I had a great lawyer, but my colleagues and employer abandoned me to the outcome of the investigation. This experience was more than just abuse. It was workplace violence.

Contemplation: How can you safely assert yourself in a volatile workplace setting without jeopardizing your safety? If you had been the target of Tom's rage, what would you have done or said?

_____

_____

_____

_____

_____

_____

_____

_____

Contemplation: Consider some of the ways your own experiences with abuse have shaped your interactions with your patients. Does a patient's history of abuse ever trigger your own memories of abuse? If so, in what ways? If not, do you feel you have distanced yourself in any way from any abuse you may have suffered? In what ways?

_____

_____

_____

_____

_____

_____

_____

As I progressed in my academic career, I realized that the academic setting was rife with such abuse, and junior faculty, women, and faculty of color were particularly vulnerable to attacks—attacks that didn't have to have any truth to them in order to be effective. I decided to leave my job because I did not see any changes in the work culture. Academic medicine had been my dream career, but this event made me think twice about chronically exposing myself to a culture that was breaking me. When I grieved the loss of my career, my husband gifted me the book, *Option B* by Sheryl Sandberg. Today, I am still working on building my own Option B. As I heal from this event, I have learned to abandon and detach from some of the behaviors and beliefs that create the physician's "professional identity" and "culture." I am learning to honor my personal sense of self before my professional sense of "survival" while still being true to my duty as a physician and my dedication to my colleagues and patients.

Reflection: Have you ever been bullied or mobbed? If so, how did the situation resolve? If it is still ongoing, what steps can you take to mitigate the abuse?

_____

_____

_____

_____

_____

_____

_____

Reflection: Have you ever witnessed someone being bullied or mobbed? If so, how did you feel? Did you want to intervene or not get involved? Did the abuse resolve or escalate? As the abuse changed, did your views about the person being abused change? Did you come to feel the abuse was deserved? If so, why? Do some people deserve abuse and others not?

_____

_____

_____

_____

_____

_____

_____

As physicians, we are trained to recognize abuse when a patient presents with signs they've been abused. We may notice abuse in others, as well, yet fail to recognize it in ourselves when we are subjected to abuse. Consider the ways in which you may extend compassion, and maybe even take steps to intervene when you recognize abuse in others.

Contemplation: What do you advise your patients who are victims of abuse? What do you tell them when they try to trivialize or dismiss their abuse as no big deal?

_____

_____

_____

_____

_____

_____

_____

Contemplation: Would you follow this same advice? Why or why not?

_____

_____

_____

_____

_____

_____

_____

_____

Contemplation: What advice would you give a colleague in a hospital system if s/he came to you for advice on how to handle an abusive situation at work, was being forced to do more work than humanely possible, or was having to sacrifice her family and social life to meet the increasingly unreasonable needs of her employer?

_____

_____

_____

_____

_____

_____

_____

Contemplation: Do you note any incongruities in your self-talk, your advice to abused patients, and your advice to colleagues feeling abused or exploited? Are you minimizing your own abuse in comparison to how you would respond to a patient or a colleague? If so, why might you view your needs as less significant than others' needs?

_____

_____

_____

_____

_____

_____

_____

Step Forward: What are three things you can proactively do to protect yourself and your staff from aggression in the work environment?

_____

_____

_____

_____

_____

_____

_____

_____

_____

As much as the healthcare system imposes limits on the time we can devote to our patients, patients themselves feel shortchanged. They may wait for hours to see us, despite having appointments, only to find we only have ten minutes with them. They may view our being late as our own doing, and our being rushed as disregard. As a result, patients often see physicians as co-conspirators in a healthcare system that puts profits over people. They may also view us as so privileged that they think we are immune to suffering.

Step Forward: How do you think patients and healthcare administrators could see us in a more realistic, and compassionate way?

_____

_____

_____

_____

_____

_____

_____

_____

_____

_____

***

The core of intimacy is sharing your trauma story.
Bessel van der Kolk

***

Step Forward: One of the most damaging aspects of being bullied or mobbed is the experience leads to internalizing the messages that we are deserving of abuse. No one deserves abuse. What are some truths about yourself and how worthy you are that you can remind yourself of if you are being mistreated?

_____

_____

_____

_____

_____

_____

_____

_____

_____

***

The wound is the place where the Light enters you.

Rumi

***

The Patient-Healer Relationship

Every patient is a surprise, but we are taught to not think about them as individuals but to treat their diagnoses. We are told to prescribe them medication, but we are not given the time to discuss the side effects or interactions with other drugs they may be taking. After a while, cynicism creeps in. Who cares if you get sued because you only spoke with this patient for just a few minutes—you can't be held liable! The less time you spend with them, the better! The more patients we see, the fewer patients we truly see.

There is also the dilemma that comes with the risk of undertreating a patient, leading to needless suffering, or overtreating them, with risking potential adverse effects like antibiotic resistance, drug interactions, or complications from medical interventions or surgeries. As a result, we may hesitate to prescribe medications, ask too many questions, or pursue aggressive treatment.

Then there are the challenging and demanding patients who use controlled substances. Unfortunately, many of these patients are disrespectful, demanding, and/or needy. If you have a lot in your patient panel, you will have more work attending to these patients, and in some states, you need to check the prescription monitoring program, yet another step for you in your busy workday. They may need a special type of help that cannot be provided in 10 mins every three months, the changes dopamine has made in many of their brains will require time and gentle care. The patient/healer relationship you and they both need is impossible to achieve in our current healthcare system.

Contemplation: As doctors, we might find ourselves working with patients who misuse substances, and as their doctors, we may be on the frontlines of cutting off their supply. When you recognize a patient has an addiction or substance abuse problem, do you feel concerned about how they will react to your advice? Do you become self-protective or judgmental? In what ways?

_____

_____

_____

_____

_____

_____

_____

_____

Contemplation: How does drug dependency or substance abuse change a patient's ability to hear your medical advice? Do you think it affects the trust between the doctor and the patient? If so, in what way? How can we restore trust among healthcare professionals and patients?

_____

_____

_____

_____

_____

_____

_____

_____

Contemplation: Have you ever felt divided on how the healthcare system accuses us of conspiring in the opioid epidemic while labeling us as having a bias against these patients if we do not prescribe the medications? What are some of the ways you feel frustrated when it comes to managing pain, treating addiction, and determining if a patient needs more medication or treatment for their addiction?

_____

_____

_____

_____

_____

_____

_____

Contemplation: Do you feel pressured by the pharmaceutical industry to prescribe their medications? Have patients ever bullied you into prescribing a medication when perhaps there was a more appropriate treatment? Discuss your experiences and thoughts on the pressure you receive from both the pharmaceutical reps and your patients to prescribe certain medications.

_____

_____

_____

_____

_____

_____

_____

Reflection: Has a patient ever fired you because you did not provide the treatment or medication they requested? If so, how did you feel about their decision? If not, has there been a time when your patient heeded your advice about a medication with the potential to be misused or abused or lead to dependency? How did you handle it?

_____

_____

_____

_____

_____

_____

_____

_____

Contemplation: Do you feel trapped by a system requiring you to see X number of patients per hour, limiting your capacity to connect and adequately communicate with the patient to help them beyond prescribing the "magic pill?" How do you manage to use your limited time to have meaningful interactions with your patients?

_____

_____

_____

_____

_____

_____

_____

_____

Contemplation: At the heart of the patient-healer relationship is listening. Every doctor has stories about their relationships with their patients—how can listening to the stories of your colleagues help you to become a more empathetic and active listener to your patients' stories?

_____

_____

_____

_____

_____

_____

_____

_____

***

Trauma does not choose a day.

***

I was in my first year of residency in my second round of inpatient rotation, and I was not very enthusiastic about it. I had already worked with my senior resident, and I knew he was not fond of me. I felt he had little constraint when prescribing meds and did not allow me to make my own decisions. The defenses I put up with him ultimately impacted my patient care.

As always, I had started my early morning rounds after the shift change. I walked into the room of one of my newly assigned patients and saw an elderly woman lying in her hospital bed, awake and alert, surrounded by IVs. One leg had been amputated years earlier, and she had developed an infection in her other foot. I had all the results and specialist recommendations I needed to tell her what was going on with her other foot, which had become infected. Her one remaining foot still helped her to see herself as human, as normal, and as a non-disabled person. I had no good news, and honestly, I did not know how to break it to her. Her medical conditions, which included diabetes, were not helping the infection in her foot heal, which had a foul odor indicating there was probably nothing we could do to save it.

I broke the news and told her that she needed the other foot amputated. She turned, stared at me with soft and gentle eyes, and asked if it could wait. I could feel her spirit sinking as we spoke, and knew she needed some comfort. I explained to her the severity of her infection and the risk of waiting. I also told her I would need to discuss it with my senior resident. "I just need to go home for a little while," she explained. "I left my cat at home alone, and if I have to stay longer, I need to find someone to take care of him." Her cat was her primary attachment. Her cat was her life, her companion, her friend. She had no other connection with life. What would happen to her cat if she did not go home and plan for extended care? I had no words.

I went back to my senior resident, and I advocated for her. But he was unmoved and said if she left, it would be against medical advice. When I informed her of his decision, she did not go home, and her foot was amputated. I never asked about her cat.

Rather than help her with her emotional needs, I disconnected from her pain. I had no words to comfort her, and I could not find the words. I shut down, rather than process my patient's emotional pain as I focused on her physical needs. Years later, I am still haunted by her pain and wonder if I should have helped her to process her pain.

Reflection: Did you ever attend to a patient's physical needs but ignored their emotional needs? If so, what were you feeling at the time? Have you ever ignored your own emotional needs when caring for your patient? What happened?

_____

_____

_____

_____

_____

_____

_____

_____

Reflection: Have you ever complied with a more experienced professional, even though you knew the patient was not well attended to? What happened, and how did you resolve, or fail to resolve, the conflict in your heart?

_____

_____

_____

_____

_____

_____

_____

_____

Reflection: Have you ever been involved in patient care where the patient's wishes were considered "against medical advice?" If so, did you think the advice truly protected the patient, or did it protect us from the dreaded medical malpractice lawsuits?

_____

_____

_____

_____

_____

_____

_____

_____

Reflection: Have you ever felt that healthcare is morally misaligned, causing damage to the most vulnerable patients and their doctors? If so, what changes are needed to provide more ethically-based healthcare and what do you feel you can do to promote such changes?

_____

_____

_____

_____

_____

_____

_____

_____

Step Forward: How do you think we can substitute the absolute power and control that the phrase "against medical advice" gives us over our patients, and use trauma-informed terms that give patients freedom and choice and recognize them as equal partners in their care?

_____

_____

_____

_____

_____

_____

_____

_____

_____

Profits Over People

We hear a lot about how the American healthcare system is not designed for patient healing. We hear less often that the American healthcare system is not intended for the wellbeing of physicians, either. Our healthcare system is designed to maximize profits, requiring physicians to see more and more patients for less and less time, work around the clock, and remain disengaged and unaffected by the endless injuries, diseases, and deaths we witness on any given day. But we are affected, while at best we're advised to focus on stress reduction and relaxation techniques. Is this the advice we'd give a patient who had been abused? Reflect on the self-talk you give yourself when you're feeling overwhelmed, put down, or badly treated in your work. Reflect, as well, on the advice you give to patients who come to you with signs of abuse or who have been traumatized by a profit-driven healthcare system.

You've been abused through medical school, and maybe even bullied, abused, or sabotaged at work. You've learned to bury your pain and push away your emotions, but in many ways, doing so has either left you feeling numb and joyless, or you have so normalized the abuse that you don't even think about it as abuse. Yet there is another way in which abuse becomes normalized and contributes to our burnout. Working in a healthcare system that puts profits over people not only limits what we can do as physicians to help our patients but sometimes that focus on profit forces physicians to make decisions that hurt or even kill their patients. At the very least, the profit-oriented healthcare system can exacerbate the suffering a patient and their family must endure. And when that happens, physicians can feel powerless at best, enraged at worst, because they know what their patient needs to stay alive and healthy, and being poor should not cost them their lives so someone else can profit.

During my residency, I traveled to South America to work for two weeks in a remote area of Ecuador in an American faith-based hospital. One hot and humid morning, a woman was sent to our hospital because she had a placenta previa and we were more equipped to deliver her baby than the small local hospital. As she passed by the nursing station, I was struck by the tall, robust woman with such a bright smile walking with so much energy and enthusiasm. After being evaluated by us, we sent her to OR for a C-Section. All went well for mom and baby, and after we closed her incision, she was rolled into her room, her big, bright smile showing how excited she was to meet her newborn, her first child.

A few hours later, we noticed her abdomen inflating like a balloon, her heart rate accelerating, and her blood pressure dropping. It was obvious she had postpartum bleeding. She was rushed into the O.R., all hands on deck, and we were all called in. I scrubbed as quickly and carefully as I could, my heart racing.

When I went in, I saw that she was already cut open. The surgical attending asked me to join the other two residents in applying pressure, moving organs, and suctioning blood in hopes of finding the cause of the bleeding. Nothing seemed to work. Many hands were inside her abdomen, and I applied as much pressure as my petite body allowed. As the sponges became soaked in blood, more were brought to me, but seconds later, they'd be soaked again. Finally, the surgeon retracted from the patient, asked a question to the anesthesiologist, and then declared, "We need to close her." The surgeon made the decision to close the abdomen and not waste more resources. The bleeding was too great; we could not see inside, and we could not identify the source of the bleeding. I came out of the O.R. and saw her husband waiting outside, sitting on the bench desperate for news. I knew things were not good, but I was not the primary surgeon or resident on the case. I turned my gaze and kept walking to the nurse station. Our attending physician told us to stay overnight at the hospital and watch over mom.

There were no heroic moves or measures because it was inevitable, she would die since we'd been unable to stop the bleeding. I never knew if my attending and surgeon explained this to the family. That night, the patient's mom kneeled in the room and with raised hands pleaded to God for a miracle. Nothing happened, there was no miracle, the bleeding continued. We gave her dopamine to keep her stable, but the more her belly grew, the more we knew how bad things were and in this remote hospital, we could not order more dopamine. Once the medication was gone, we had nothing else to give her. She died before sunrise. The baby was sent home with her husband but before his wife's body would be released, he had to pay the American hospital for all the services. The grieving family sold their car to bury their loved one.

This story still makes me cry. I had witnessed multiple C-Sections before and knew of the dangers of postpartum bleeding, but in watching this new mother die the reality of maternal deaths, and our limitations as physicians, really struck me. I was also struck by the coldness and detachment of my attending physicians as they calmly tried to save her. They had to make extremely difficult decisions as they considered how to best utilize their limited resources based on each patient's chances of survival. Why use all the medication on one patient unlikely to survive if it could be saved for a patient with better odds? And though I knew that if she'd given birth in the United States, she would have had a better chance at survival, I was stunned at the refusal of the American hospital to release her body without payment for her healthcare. That story revealed to me a great contradiction in our care—we are limited by our resources, by the profits our healthcare system demands, and by the human body, which we cannot always control.

Contemplation: In medicine we are all part of stories where witness death, pain, and suffering. Have you ever been involved in a particularly disturbing case that haunts you to this day? What happened? Describe the experience, your feelings at the time, and how writing about it feels to you now.

_____

_____

_____

_____

_____

_____

_____

Reflection: Have you ever experienced a simple and routine procedure turn out badly or become a tragedy? How did you feel about it, and did the experience change in any way the way you approach your treatment and/or interactions with patients?

_____

_____

_____

_____

_____

_____

_____

Contemplation: Have you felt the healthcare system puts profit over the health of people? If so, in what ways? Did you feel you could speak out against such policies or actions or witness a colleague do so? What emotions did the experience stir up? If you've witnessed a colleague speak up, did you feel empowered to speak up in the same way, or fearful of doing so?

_____

_____

_____

_____

_____

_____

_____

_____

Reflection: Have you witnessed any inhumane acts motivated by profit over people? What happened, and did you feel you could say or do anything to support your patient over profit?

_____

_____

_____

_____

_____

_____

_____

_____

Reflection: Have you ever helped a patient, thought all was well, but then learned the patient died? How did that make you feel and what did you do to process the loss (take a walk, write, discuss with colleagues, self-medicate)? How did your colleagues respond? Do you feel they were supportive?

_____

_____

_____

_____

_____

_____

_____

Contemplation: Do you have experience with the healthcare system of other countries? If yes, how do you think these systems contrast? Do you think any of the difference makes the practice of medicine easier for physicians and provides greater care to patients?

_____

_____

_____

_____

_____

_____

_____

There are many challenges with our current health system and how it has been evolving. These challenges can be different for each one of us. But one thing we share is an agreement that the current system is too complex, and change is needed. It has been well documented that these challenges need to be addressed systemically because otherwise, the problems will not be solved. Yet at times, society and culture have suggested that physicians are at fault. Yet no one doctor can do it alone, not even a team of physicians and administrators can change the system overnight so that it works better for patients and physicians. This sense of powerlessness leaves doctors feeling trapped—we recognize the system isn't working, but don't know how to create change. Dr. Dan Siegel recommends using the acronym COAL to observe yourself and the environment: Curiosity, Openness, Acceptance, and Love. Think about these qualities as you sit in a contemplative examination for the next exercise.

Contemplation: What do you find the most challenging in our current health system?

_____

_____

_____

_____

_____

_____

_____

_____

Step Forward: What solutions do you see for these?

Challenges	Solutions
Little time to comprehensively assess patient	_Move to cash-based or value-based practice model_

Step Forward: What steps can you take to move toward your ideal health system and implement the solutions?

_____

_____

_____

_____

_____

_____

_____

_____

_____

Step Forward: In what ways can you contribute to creating a functional and healthy healthcare system?

_____

_____

_____

_____

_____

_____

_____

_____

_____

_____

***

Freeing yourself was one thing, claiming ownership of
that freed self was another.
Toni Morrison, Beloved

***

Lies That Lead You

After events like the loss of a patient, the downfall or suicide of a colleague, or the abuse of a patient, our trauma response can shift us into a distorted mentality. We might deny the trauma, believing everything is for the best. More commonly, we might become cynical, believing everything and everyone is bad. We tend to create negative thoughts and beliefs that we project onto similar circumstances and, at times, onto ourselves. These negative thought patterns are lies we tell ourselves which distort reality and can limit us and not allow us to risk again. They can also lead to anxiety, depression, stress, low self-esteem, and difficulty resolving conflicts.

One of the biggest lies that physicians come to believe as we become enculturated in the medical system is that healthcare in the United States does not work because we do not work hard enough. We are expected to prove the value of our work through documentation and billing codes, while more and more codes are developed that we are expected to master. And please, no complaining or displays of vulnerability! If we communicate that we need help, we risk our jobs and reputations because we aren't supposed to need help. If we make mistakes, we are considered not worthy of being a part of the "doctor club." We melt into loneliness and silence, which just amplifies a false narrative in our minds. And if you need to navigate medical malpractice claims, you are at risk of developing PTSD or severe depression that could lead to suicide. Medicine teaches us to leave emotions undisturbed, but subconsciously our emotions still govern who we are. We are, somehow, expected to normalize our trauma and forget we are humans—imperfect, vulnerable, and limited.

Many physicians struggle. Medicine creates a tension between being an honored member of a noble profession centered on helping others and finding ourselves on a crazy cycle where we can never keep up with the demands of the system and patients' false expectations. We suffer in silence, afraid to admit that we are not okay. But it's okay to not be okay. Even healers need healing.

Reflection: Have you ever needed help to make it through the day but had no outlet or place to go because you feared repercussions to your job and medical license? Did you receive that help? Describe the help you wanted, what you did or wanted to do to receive that help, and the fears you felt. Did those fears ever come to pass? If so, in what way?

_____

_____

_____

_____

_____

_____

_____

_____

Contemplation: Has normalizing trauma, or not thinking about it, made its impact on your body, mind, and emotions go away, or has that trauma continued to live inside you? If so, in what ways?

_____

_____

_____

_____

_____

_____

_____

_____

As a product of traumatic events in medicine, what negative thoughts are
getting stuck in your head?

_____

_____

_____

_____

_____

_____

_____

Step Forward: Could any of these negative thoughts be transformed into
positive ones? If so, how could you reframe them?

_____

_____

_____

_____

_____

_____

_____

_____

_____

Step Forward: As you come to understand that these negative thoughts are lies that are holding you back while you continue to practice medicine and serve your patients, what positive *truths* about who you are do you need to hold on to?

_____

_____

_____

_____

_____

_____

_____

_____

How can you keep these truths close to you as reminders?

_____

_____

_____

_____

_____

***

Trauma creates change you don't choose.
Healing is about making the change you do choose.
Michelle Rosenthal

***

Notes

Notes

PART TWO

Healing Your Trauma

Containment, Boundaries, and Detachment

As physicians, we work hard to meet other people's needs and expectations. We are taught that doing so is the right thing to do, but we are not taught healthy containment. Containment means safeguarding others from our own emotions, unresolved issues, and needs. As children we may learn to contain all our emotions, never releasing anything but containing it all inside. Or we might learn to unleash it all, let our anger, our needs, and our fears fly, totally uncontained. To have healthy containment means to recognize that we need to exercise restraint, without shutting down emotionally.

Containment goes hand in hand with boundaries. Our boundaries are where we establish the limits of what we will and won't accept from others. A lack of boundaries could mean sharing everything with our patients and colleagues, invading their physical space inappropriately, saying whatever is on our minds. Poor boundaries can also mean letting others do the same to us—sharing personal information inappropriately, asking inappropriate and personal questions, touching us without permission. Another way in which our boundaries might be weak is in lacking the confidence to say no, to express our legitimate concerns, or to tell someone we aren't comfortable with how they are treating us or speaking to us.

It's important to establish clear boundaries and to embrace healthy containment as we respect the boundaries of others. Yet as physicians, we want to create positive feelings in our relationships with our patients and colleagues, so we often find ourselves saying Yes, when the best answer is No. We may have to examine the motivation of our patients and colleagues before responding. We must also establish clear expectations of the relationship and our respective roles. Yet saying no to a patient might cause our patient ratings to decline or our colleagues to dislike us.

Contemplation: Have there been times when you felt you allowed someone to violate your boundaries, or you violated your own boundaries by caving in to someone else's demands? How did you feel, and what prevented you from being more clear about your boundaries? Remember, you are not writing in this journal to scold yourself, but to explore your obstacles and potential.

_____

_____

_____

_____

_____

_____

_____

_____

Contemplation: Have you had experiences at work that reflected a lack of poor boundaries you felt unable to set for yourself? What happened and how did you feel?

_____

_____

_____

_____

_____

_____

_____

_____

Contemplation: Have there been times when you've felt too contained, unable to feel anything, or insufficiently contained, letting it all fly? What happened? How did you feel?

_____

_____

_____

_____

_____

_____

_____

_____

Step Forward: What three boundaries do you need to keep in mind, every day as a physician?

_____

_____

_____

_____

_____

_____

_____

_____

Contemplation: At times people will walk over your boundaries, we cannot control others. I always say, you can have a fence, but a thief might still come and steal from you. It was not that you did not have a good enough fence, it was that there was a thief nearby. So now, think about how you feel when someone walks over your fence.

_____

_____

_____

_____

_____

_____

_____

_____

Step Forward: What are some ways you can clarify to others what your boundaries are if you feel someone is transgressing them? Imagine if that person is a superior or another doctor with more seniority. How can you feel confident in your boundaries, without jeopardizing your security?

Similar to boundaries and containment is detachment. Detachment is the process of putting a bubble in place between yourself and someone or something that damages you in some way. As physicians, we engage in benevolent detachment every day, by caring and engaging with the suffering of our patients. We have discussed how doing so can lead us to shut down our emotions, but if we were to fully engage with their suffering, we would be overwhelmed. We are less trained to let go of our attachments to our egos, our careers, money, and people in our lives who emotionally exhaust us.

_____

_____

_____

_____

_____

_____

_____

_____

_____

Step Forward: How can you benevolently detach from the people, things, and thoughts that overwhelm or exhaust you?

_____

_____

_____

Know Your Values

As physicians, we are expected to put the patient's welfare over our self-interest. But this value is only half the picture; self-neglect will not make us better doctors; much less fix the sick care we provide. Yet society believes the "good doctor" is always available and willing to work long, endless hours. Moreover, many still see the physician as the enemy, something that became particularly apparent during the COVID epidemic, when so many people resisted the care they needed or even denied that they had COVID. Even worse, many doctors have expressed feeling betrayed by their patients, because they sacrificed their lives to treat them during the pandemic, while some of our patients would not even wear their masks.

Patients and healthcare administrators place us in a double bind to serve two masters while ignoring our basic needs and compromising our values, moving away from the reasons we became physicians. This double bind can seem like dual loyalty. You try to serve your patients while also producing for your employer and the insurance companies, all the while knowing that our jobs depend on patient scores and reviews which don't always correspond to our ideals of good patient care. To survive this tightrope we're forced to walk, many doctors become ambivalent to their values—suppressing their own values to please others, often out of necessity.

When it comes to our values, being clear on what these values are will guide us in making wise decisions to live true to our persona. Identifying our values will help us avoid internal conflicts as we move closer to becoming genuine healers. This is not because there are right or wrong values. It is just that knowing our values and making choices and actions consistent with these values—to the extent we can—will help us achieve the life we envision and practice medicine more sustainably.

Contemplation: What are your top 5 **professional** values?

_____

_____

_____

_____

_____

What does each mean to you? In other words, what do these values say about who you are, or what they mean for how you see the world? For example, if you indicate that "providing good patient care" is one of your top values, which might mean, "I care about my patients," "I take my role as physician seriously," or "I went into medicine to heal people." Some of your values might reflect your views on our healthcare system or your identity as a physician. This reflection isn't necessarily going to be easy, and that's the point—by reflecting on your values, their meanings, and how your values as a physician are connected to your personal values or sense of identity, you will begin to discern ways in which you do live your values in your work, and the ways in which you sometimes feel you must make compromises.

_____

_____

_____

_____

_____

What are your top 5 **personal** values?

_____

_____

_____

_____

_____

What does each of these values mean to you?

_____

_____

_____

_____

_____

Contemplation: Are your values supported by the healthcare system in which you work? In what ways are your values supported by the organization you work for? In what ways do you feel those values are not supported? How can you stay true to your values? What do you need to make this happen? What is getting in the way of meeting these needs?

_____

_____

_____

_____

_____

_____

_____

_____

Now complete these sentences:

To stay true to my value of _____, I

need _____.

The biggest obstacle to this need is _____

_____.

To stay true to my value of _____, I

need _____.

The biggest obstacle to this need is _____

_____.

To stay true to my value of _____, I

need _____.

The biggest obstacle to this need is _____

_____.

To stay true to my value of _____, I

need _____.

The biggest obstacle to this need is _____

_____.

To stay true to my value of _____, I

need _____.

The biggest obstacle to this need is _____

_____.

Step Forward: How can knowing your values help you make wise choices
about your medical career?

_____

_____

_____

_____

_____

_____

_____

_____

_____

_____

Step Forward: How can these values help you make wise choices about the care you deliver to your patients?

_____

_____

_____

_____

_____

_____

***

Your beliefs become your thoughts,
Your thoughts become your words,
Your words become your actions,
Your actions become your habits,
Your habits become your values,
Your values become your Destiny.

***

Know Your Needs

After a traumatic event, our brains are highjacked. Thinking becomes foggy, and it is difficult to know what our bodies need as we continue to live. Our brains are disconnected from our bodies, and survival becomes the default way of living. In order to feel safe, pay attention to your needs. The hidden medical school curricula taught us to ignore our needs. We learned that having needs was a weakness and a lack of resiliency. We were trained to ignore our basic physiological needs like eating when hungry, voiding when needed, and sleeping at regular hours. And we were trained to erase our emotional needs altogether.

It's especially ironic that we are taught to ignore our needs, when the process of becoming a physician is so inherently stressful, particularly when the many demands of young adulthood hit us all at once. Extended exposure to stress, especially to a variety of stressors at the same time— any combination of the vast existential menu of life events like moving, marriage, divorce, a demanding job, the loss of a loved one, having children, and caring for them—adds up to a state of extreme exhaustion that leads to what we call burnout. Physician wellness is seen as depression, anxiety, suicidality, burnout, compassion fatigue, and moral injury—yet these professional impacts are viewed as personal problems. But we are not the problem. Systemic brokenness is a problem at times too large to tackle. Many experiences in medicine, from education to practice, lead to repetitive traumatic responses. This trauma response is not being recognized, spoken to, or treated. These traumatic responses to events in medicine are related to external stressors rather than to our intrinsic qualities. It is not your fault! The entire medical system needs to change. But no one can change that system alone. What we can do is reconnect to our own needs.

By reconnecting to our needs, we connect to our bodies, and as we connect to our bodies, we tap into the wisdom of our bodies. Trauma recovery teaches us to develop kindness toward our bodies, which all too often become neglected, if not abused, by the stress of our jobs. Try the simple reflection below to create a rhythmic dance between the sensations in your body and what your body is telling you.

Contemplation:

I feel _____

therefore, I need _____

I feel _____

therefore, I need _____

I feel _____

therefore, I need _____

I feel _____

therefore, I need _____

I feel _____

therefore, I need _____

You can do the above contemplation every time you find yourself lost in a decision-making point. Consider printing out the phrase, and keeping it in your wallet, or in your desk drawer, anyplace where you can retrieve it quickly and reflect on it. Over time, you won't even need to retrieve it. Thinking of your feelings and what it is you need will become automatic in times of stress.

Step Forward: What are some ways you can honor your physiological needs, at work and outside of work? List ten, starting with the top three—the most obvious, easy, and necessary. Be specific. Don't say, eat healthier food. You've always known you need to do that, but if you haven't been doing so, writing it down won't make it happen. But if you wrote, "Fill half my plate with vegetables," that's more specific—you just might do that. Similarly, instead of "exercise more," or "sleep more," if you write, "take a walk each evening," "lift weights for five minutes a day," "go to bed fifteen minutes earlier," or "stop drinking caffeine after work," you just might do it. Give yourself manageable ways to meet your needs.

_____

_____

_____

_____

_____

_____

_____

_____

_____

_____

It's common to neglect our needs because we're tired, especially after we've come home from a busy day at work, or when we have a couple of days off and want to just unwind and do nothing, but have so much to do at home, errands to catch up on, a family to spend time with. We're depleted. Yet think about times when you've been exhausted, but something demands or catches your attention, and you forget all about how tired you are. It might be a visit from a friend, a drive out to the country, a book you're reading, a painting you've been working on, or playing with your children. These are energizing activities, and they vary for each of us. What things energize you?

Contemplation: Make a list of everything that energizes you. Think about things in your work environment that you could incorporate into your daily work. Include something that you can use after a busy day of work to add positive energy to the few hours of your day left. It's okay if you can't think of ten things. Just list as many as you can think of and add to it as new ideas arise.

_____

_____

_____

_____

_____

_____

_____

_____

_____

Now make a list of everything that depletes your energy. These can be in the job or stressors outside the job.

_____

_____

_____

_____

_____

_____

_____

_____

_____

Step Forward: Take a look at the list above. How can you move away from depletion? How can you focus on adding vitality and positive energy to your life?

_____

_____

_____

_____

_____

_____

_____

_____

_____

Contemplation: Think about your needs, do you feel they are unique to you or do you feel they are needs you share with your professional community or some group within the community? Describe these needs and how they are unique and/or shared.

_____

_____

_____

_____

_____

_____

_____

_____

Step Forward: To the extent your needs are unique to you, how can you meet those needs without feeling "different" from the group? How can you take care of yourself?

_____

_____

_____

_____

_____

_____

_____

_____

_____

Step Forward: To the extent your needs are shared, are there resources you can turn to that would help? If not, is there some action you can take to raise awareness and help yourself and others have these needs addressed? Be creative, consider small steps, as well as big ones.

_____

_____

_____

_____

_____

_____

_____

_____

_____

_____

***

We work against our needs to survive the madness of medicine.

***

Triggers Flooded!

We all are at times flooded by memories through dreams, recurrent memories, and sometimes even flashbacks, which are particularly vivid memories we're unable to control. Our bodies often respond to these traumatic memories through butterflies in our stomach, palpitations, perspiration, tears, trembling, hyperventilating, and other sympathetic and parasympathetic responses. When physicians experience these symptoms after a traumatic event, they usually do not seek help—even if they'd urge their patients to do so. We are trained to get used to pain and suffering as a normal part of the profession. Physicians can develop a quiet and calm exterior, while internal chaos of the highjacked brain is operating on a different level altogether. When something we encounter triggers one of these traumatic memories—even unconsciously—we relive them.

Can you identify any triggers that provoke an unwelcoming response in your mind and body? Triggers are unique from person to person, but all are valid. Not just a thought that pops into our mind, a trigger almost always involves one of the senses—something we see, hear, taste, smell, or touch—that brings to mind the past. A trigger can be positive, such as the smell of flowers bringing to mind pleasant childhood days spent in the garden, or they can be negative, such as the sight of a bullet wound bringing a flood of traumatic memories from a mass shooting whose victims you attended. Someone might look or speak like an abuser who tormented you, or a mild criticism might trigger anxiety from a cruel rebuke of a professor or supervising physician. The triggers themselves don't cause the emotion, but the memories they trigger do.

These stimuli can be at work or outside your work. You might be immediately aware of them, or you might just feel that something caused you anxiety, and you can't quite put your finger on it. If the anxiety appears seemingly out of nowhere, it was probably triggered by something, something so seemingly trivial you may already have forgotten it. But when you do sense you've been triggered, pay attention to the places in your body where the response happens. Does your jaw clench? Does your heartbeat increase? Do you feel a sudden tension? Note the somatic responses to your triggers as they arise. By becoming aware that these feelings are responses to a trigger, they often diminish.

Stimulus	Body Response
A colleague raises the tone of voice to you.	My heart starts racing like a horse.

Reflection: Can you recall something that triggered you, positively or negatively, in recent weeks? What happened? Were you immediately aware of the trigger, or did something gnaw at you before you could recall what it was? What was the response? Describe your body's response, as well as an intrusive memory.

_____

_____

_____

_____

_____

_____

_____

_____

Create!: It might be hard to put words to your bodily response. If this happens, try to imagine a color that represents your feelings. We often think of "feeling blue" or "seeing red," but there may be other colors that capture your emotions. Be creative as you tap into this reflection—and note any changes in your body as you do so. Draw what comes up as you recall your triggers, capturing what and where you feel your emotions in your body. And if you feel stuck, just have fun with colors!

Reflection: Have you noticed any pattern in your triggers? A pattern might be a set of cues that trigger a response to a specific trauma you find yourself reliving, or the triggers might be from a specific source, such as a location or person, and you may not even be clear on why they provoke these responses. The pattern may or may not be related to an event having nothing to do with your medical education or career. If you have noticed such a pattern, what is it?

_____

_____

_____

_____

_____

_____

_____

Triggers can provoke an emotional or physiological response that we cannot initially control, but as we build awareness, we can manage these triggers both directly and indirectly, so that the response is less stressful. A direct response might be to disengage from the trigger. For example, in conversation with a colleague, they say something that triggers a previous conversation with someone else who was unnecessarily cruel to you. Although this particular colleague is not being cruel, their tone or wording has put you on the defensive, and you find yourself reacting not to this colleague, but to the memory of the other colleague who treated you so badly. As you notice yourself _reacting_ more than _interacting_, you realize you might turn a minor issue into something bigger. A direct response could be, "I'm not feeling well today. How about if we loop back on the topic tomorrow?" Other direct responses might be to remove yourself from the setting that triggers you or to tell someone that something they are saying or doing, or that you are doing, is bringing back these memories.

Step Forward: Thinking back to the responses you provided in the previous questions, what are some **direct** responses you might try if this same scenario repeats?

_____

_____

_____

_____

_____

_____

_____

_____

_____

_____

Step Forward: Indirect approaches to managing triggers include taking steps to minimize the stress response, such as going for a walk, spending time in nature to calm yourself and become grounded, meditating, exercising, or engaging in a hobby or artwork. What are some indirect approaches you would like to turn to when you feel triggered?

_____

_____

_____

_____

_____

_____

_____

_____

_____

_____

Sometimes we can't disengage from our triggers. If you've been physically or sexually abused yourself, you may well encounter patients who have been physically or sexually abused, and caring for them triggers you, but you can't turn them away. Or the trigger might be so common that the only way to avoid it altogether would be to seal yourself away in your home and never step out the door, turn on the TV or open a book. In these cases, it helps to be able to remind yourself that the event, environment, or act that is triggering you is something new and not related to the original event. It is not the trauma you experienced, but instead, it is your past trauma affecting your present as you recall the original trauma.

Step Forward: How might you take that reminder one step further with a mantra that you recall in times of triggering? For example, you might remind yourself by saying, "I'm safe, and this moment is something new. My anxiety is just a memory poking its head into the present. Be gone, bad memory, be gone. I'm safe." What is a mantra or reminder you can say silently to yourself in those moments of triggering?

_____

_____

_____

_____

_____

_____

_____

_____

_____

_____

***

A colleague speaks over me. I feel anger, my ears turn red and hot.
Knowing what we feel, where we feel it, and why is the beginning of the
journey of managing our world and gaining agency.

***

Step Forward: One of the most empowering steps a target of abuse can
take is to engage in courageous action. Trauma healing is about regaining our
sense of power and control, in other words, agency. What are some of the
steps that you can take, whether small or big, to exercise your own agency?
How can you rewrite the narrative of your life from victim to agent?

_____

_____

_____

_____

_____

_____

_____

_____

_____

Putting Your Safety First

Working in a profession that exposes us to trauma daily requires us to gain—and to regain—a sense of safety and security in our minds, bodies, and emotions. After a traumatic event, our amygdala activates the flight, fight or freeze response. The amygdala captures these traumatic events and replays them, reducing our neocortex—our thinking mind—as we live in a near-constant state of flight, fight, or freeze. As a physician, you will often interact with your patients and colleagues with a sense of danger, anxiety, and stress, your body in constant preparation to defend against attack. Feeling safe helps quiet our amygdala and raises the volume of the prefrontal cortex. This slow shift in our brains allows us to walk, even if slowly, toward reclaiming our life following a traumatic or highly stressful event.

In this section, try to think about gaining and regaining your sense of safety in this broken world. How can you manage your triggers? Remember, this journal is for your eyes alone. Write down what you really feel and think. Remember that if reflections are strenuous, you can pause. After each contemplation, I recommend you take a nice slow deep breath. Use the power of breath as a tool to transition back into life.

***

What happens in this world is beyond our control, but we always have choices, and we never lose all our power.

***

Many years ago, psychologist Abraham Maslow included safety as one of the basic human needs, yet we often forget our own needs in medicine. We focus on creating security for the patient, and perhaps we assume their security guarantees our safety.

One winter morning, a new young female patient was part of my busy schedule. She had come to the appointment with her mother, who sat in the corner as I examined my patient. The young woman had lost a lot of weight, looked pale and sad, and had little energy. She was taking high doses of opioids for chronic back pain. As I spoke to her, I advised her that we should try other options for her pain. I addressed all her medical concerns and wanted to help her manage her pain while also reducing her use of opioids. As I explained this treatment plan, she slammed a table across the examination room. She stood up, screamed, "Fuck you!" then stormed out of the room cursing, crying, and yelling as she fled down the hallway. Her mother, sitting calmly, explained to me that this was how she reacted every time a health professional addressed her use of opioids for pain management. She then berated me for not treating her daughter for her pain, arguing that opioids were the only option. When I disagreed and tried to persuade her of the dangers of continuing the opioids, the mother stood up and left, convinced I was unwilling to help her daughter.

The mother undoubtedly reinforced her daughter's conviction that opioids were necessary. Both mother and daughter could not hear my unwelcome message. But the daughter's tirade did not end with her storming out of the room. She screamed at my staff, and her mother was not friendly to anyone in the office. I feared for my safety, and for my staff. There was nothing I could do to protect myself. I felt not only disrespected but defeated. I drove home that night thinking about the encounter and why my patient had reacted so violently. As a physician, I knew her reaction was related to her use of opioids. But as a human, a woman who had been targeted with violence and insults, I kept wondering, what did I do wrong? Now, years later, this encounter has shaped the way I view my patients. When I see patients on certain medications, the warning bell inside me turns on. Will they be set off if I fail to refill their medications? But I no longer give in to such anxieties. Now when I sense patients becoming aggressive, I take a deep breath and try to think of a strategy to manage these challenging encounters. Sometimes I am successful and sometimes I fail at keeping the patient happy, yet I know that ultimately, I am not responsible for someone else's happiness.

Reflection: Has a patient ever become violent with you or your staff? If so, how did it affect you? Did it impact the rest of your day? Your interactions with other patients? Did you dream about it or think about it days or even weeks later?

_____

_____

_____

_____

_____

_____

_____

_____

Reflection: How did you handle the situation? If you don't feel you handled it well, what might you have done differently?

_____

_____

_____

_____

_____

_____

_____

_____

Trauma fragments us. When the body divides traits and feelings and groups them into smaller sections, keeping some of them hidden until a safe space for expression is provided, our authenticity is affected. To feel safe, we hide parts of ourselves almost like multiple personalities that emerge depending on the social interaction.

Trauma separates us from safety. Lack of emotional and physiological security will activate the fight, flight, or freeze response. Your interaction in the world will be focused on your survival, affecting all your relationships. Using tools to start your relaxation response will aid your body in feeling safe. Safety will shift how we relate and behave in the workplace with our family and friends. Since trauma does not choose a day to visit us, we need to create a way of life that propels us despite the chronic stress we carry. The fragmentation we experience separates us from the essence of being human. Our medical education was about action, working long hours, and memorizing enormous quantities of information to just regurgitate hours later. We were expected to learn science, do research, volunteer, and build a resume that would help us compete for that dream position in our selected residency program. All this perfectionistic striving draws us far from who we first were when we were drawn to medicine. Regaining the essence of our humanity and authenticity—and not boxing away parts of ourselves for differing social contexts—is integral to our healing.

To become our authentic selves and integrate our broken parts into a healthy whole, we need to start feeling safe in our bodies and minds.

Contemplation: In what ways do you fragment yourself in different social contexts? Describe how the self you bring to work differs from the self you are at home, the self you are in public, with friends, and with families.

_____

_____

_____

_____

_____

_____

_____

_____

Contemplation: Do you feel safe bringing your authentic self to work? If so, what is it about your work environment that nurtures that sense of safety? If not, what do you fear might happen if your patients, colleagues, and supervisors worked alongside your authentic self?

_____

_____

_____

_____

_____

_____

_____

_____

Feeling safe means living without fear, but to live without fear we must first confront our fears. Medical training teaches us to keep our fears under control. Who wants a doctor full of fear and insecurity? Medical training's silent rule is "fake it till you make it." We learn to push forward and ignore our bodies and emotions, and we learn to white-knuckle it. Fear is a warning sign that says STOP. At times, this warning signal can keep us from moving forward when we need to move forward in reality. We need to listen to it at other times, remembering we are humans and must STOP.

Contemplation: Have you noticed in what situations you feel fear? Is there an actual danger to your safety? What situations trigger your fears and how do you respond?

_____

_____

_____

_____

_____

_____

_____

Reflection: Do you remember times during your training when you had to white knuckle through a difficult situation, but fear drained all your energy? What happened?

_____

_____

_____

_____

_____

_____

_____

_____

Step Forward: When we are afraid or feel anxious, our fear or anxiety is often out of proportion to any real risk, or they involve our imaginations running wild with what might happen or could happen but are not happening. Our imaginations rule our emotions, rather than reality. What can you do to separate the reality of the risks you face from the emotion of fear?

_____

_____

_____

_____

_____

_____

_____

_____

_____

_____

Contemplation: Our amygdala manages our fears, alerting us to potential danger (real and imagined). While this fear response may be maladaptive when it causes us undue fear and anxiety, our ability to feel fear is an evolutionary trait that protects us from danger. Managing your fear involves recognizing when your amygdala is responding to a real versus a perceived threat. In what situations, as a physician, do you need to stop when your amygdala flashes, WARNING?

_____

_____

_____

_____

_____

_____

_____

_____

***

You must crawl into your wounds to discover where your fears are because once the bleeding starts, the cleaning can begin.

Tori Amos

***

Contemplation: Where do you feel the safest, physically, and emotionally? Think of a place or space where you felt safe and protected as a child, or where you feel safest in your life now. Perhaps that place is your home, of a space in your home, such as your bed, or the kitchen where you enjoy creating, or the garden, where you enjoy bringing color and life to your world. Perhaps that space is in the arms of your partner. Give some thought to the many places where you feel safest.

_____

_____

_____

_____

_____

_____

_____

_____

Step Forward: How can you create this environment at work? Is there a way that you can create a safe space in your office, or in your mind? What might that space look or feel like?

_____

_____

_____

_____

_____

_____

_____

_____

_____

Grieving to Grow

Losses, we have had many. As physicians, we are experts at life and death. We have witnessed the many losses of our patients, and we have our own losses we must grieve. I had a powerful experience that taught me this lesson early in my medical career.

In medical school, I was fascinated with obstetrics. Something about bringing babies into this world and sharing a very intimate experience with women brought me great joy. In my last year of residency, I decided to embark on an elective in high-risk obstetrics. It was spring, and nature was coming alive. My days were 12-hour shifts, but I was always excited to get out early to enjoy some of the great spring weather. But there was a day I decided to stay until late at night. That night I cried with the moon as my only witness.

It was late afternoon, and we were getting ready to change shifts and sign out to the night team. Suddenly, we noticed the monitor of a new patient. I headed to the triage room to quickly access the patient and let the night team know the situation. The nurse told me she could not locate a fetal heartbeat; the patient was not having contractions and reported her baby had not moved for the past couple of hours. She had had the same issue the day before and was seen in another facility but had been sent home. We pulled the ultrasound machine to better assess the heartbeat. The baby's heart was not beating. I did a quick vaginal exam. She was almost fully dilated but with no contractions. My attending physician came in to ask what was happening. I quickly explained. She looked at the TOCO monitor and then completed a quick ultrasound, then quickly looked at mom and broke the news. She stepped outside to call the attending nightshift.

The night team made their own assessment and then gave mom her options. She could either have a C-Section or be induced with Pitocin once her water was artificially broken. The male attending was honest, brutally honest. He asked her if she would want to go through all the pain of labor if her baby would be born dead. He framed the question as if she would be a fool to do so, selfish even, when we could just slice her belly open and dispose of her child. Alone and shamed, she opted for C-Section.

The night fellow came to me and asked me if I wanted to stay and assist in the C-Section since she was my patient. I said yes, not knowing what that meant for me. I was full of emotions—and I let them all out in the call room. "What the fuck had just happened?" I cursed. Mom had gone to another hospital, and the baby was found to have decelerations, but she had just been hydrated and sent home. Why had they done that? But I knew why. She did not have insurance and there were no baby's father or family members with her. She was easy to dismiss, a patient who couldn't pay, a patient having a baby all by herself. I fumed and ranted at the injustice. Nobody judged me, but few words were offered to help me process my pain in light of this injustice. When I'd exhausted my rage, I stepped into the OR to deliver a floppy blue baby. It was a difficult and painful experience for everyone present, made even worse knowing this grieving mother had no one to support her.

I left to go "home." I was staying with one of the program attendings. It was my birthday, and she had prepared a little celebration for me. I arrived, the table full of food and cake. She knew what had happened and recognized I was not in party mode. But she told me, "Well, eat; not all is easy."

I sat there by myself, not knowing what to do with my emotions. The following day while on rounds I visited the grieving mom. She had even fewer emotions than me. She was alone. I asked if she wanted me to call anyone. Her answer was soft but firm. "No," she said. My heart was tender toward her, but she was stable post-C-Section, and my job was done. I left her alone, knowing that throughout my career there would be more grieving mothers whose babies I couldn't save, and more lives lost because a patient couldn't pay, or was looked down upon, or who just had the misfortune to be sent home when someone should have helped them.

You have your own stories of such losses. Patients whose grief you felt in your bones. Patients you couldn't help. Losses of your own that left you feeling vanquished. Whatever your loss, or the losses you have witnessed, it's important to grieve—to allow yourself the gift of passing through the stages from shock to acceptance.

Reflection: Have you ever witnessed a colleague give bad news bluntly and not provide emotional care to their patient? What happened?

_____

_____

_____

_____

_____

_____

_____

_____

Contemplation: How do you deliver bad news to your patients? Would you prefer a different approach? If so, what keeps you from it?

_____

_____

_____

_____

_____

_____

_____

_____

Reflection: Have you ever felt intense emotions while working, but your colleagues couldn't help you? If so, do you remember what happened? Were you able to find help elsewhere?

_____

_____

_____

_____

_____

_____

_____

Reflection: After the death of a patient, have you felt guilty, powerless, filled with self-doubt, isolated, worthless, or despairing? How have you managed your emotions?

_____

_____

_____

_____

_____

_____

_____

Reflection: Have you ever witnessed a patient not being able to receive the care they needed because of their ability to pay for services? What happened? Did you do or say anything? Did you feel safe to do so?

_____

_____

_____

_____

_____

_____

_____

_____

From the time we enter medical school, we experience loss. We lose time from our families and friends as we study around the clock, compromising our health. We lose financial security to pay for our costly education, forcing us to take demanding and constricted jobs to repay our student loans. We lose more time from our personal lives as we work eighty-hour weeks, sometimes spending more time in front of computers than in front of patients, only to find we've lost our autonomy as physicians. Insurance companies, corporate policies, and metrics dictate how we care for our patients. We lose our capacity to say NO to patients as patient satisfaction scores, profits, and internet reviews become more important than evidence-based medicine. We have lost patients and have gained more consumers who seek our services while distrusting us. We lose our privacy as medical boards ask questions about our health. We lose connection to our emotions as we are taught to distance ourselves emotionally and create protective boundaries of professionalism.

Reflection: Write a list of your losses including your relationships, finances, time, health, and soul.

_____

_____

_____

_____

_____

_____

_____

_____

_____

Step Forward: Now look back on your list and think about the meaning of each loss and how these losses have affected your identity.

_____

_____

_____

_____

_____

_____

_____

_____

_____

_____

Contemplation: What emotions come up? Which losses are hardest to accept? Which losses are the easiest to move on from?

_____

_____

_____

_____

_____

_____

_____

Reflection: As we advance in our careers as physicians, one of our losses is our autonomy, as we lose control over our lives and jobs. In what ways do you feel you have autonomy at work and in your personal life, and in what ways do you feel you lost your autonomy?

_____

_____

_____

_____

_____

_____

_____

Step Forward: How might you increase your autonomy at work and in your personal life? List some ways you might think and act with more autonomy.

_____

_____

_____

_____

_____

_____

_____

_____

_____

_____

_____

***

We may think we can control our grief, our terror, or our shame by
remaining silent, but naming offers the possibility of a
different kind of control.
Bessel van der Kolk

***

We need to grieve to grow. As physicians, we suffer for patients who die
because we cannot help. We need to grieve the injustices of a medical
system that delivers sick care with limited resources. We also grieve for the
life we have lost by entering a career that robs us of our personal life. We
grieve for the years we have lost with our loved ones as we focus on our
medical profession. Without grieving, we cannot make space for something
new in our lives. Grief helps us to honor our losses and embrace change.

Create!: Write a letter to yourself. Think about that young, energized, and hopeful medical student you once were. What can you say to the younger you? What have you lost since entering the medical profession but also learned?

Advocating for Self

Medicine teaches us to be quiet and not complain. Complaining is seen as being disruptive or not caring enough about patient care. If we are perceived as disruptive, our licenses might be compromised, or we might be labeled "bad" doctors and called into the hospital committee for discipline. If we raise concerns about discrimination, harassment, or even concerns about patient care, we will be perceived as "complainers," "tattletales," "whistleblowers," or "troublemakers." We can even face retaliation.

We are taught to advocate for our patients but never to advocate for our physical needs, better work conditions, or different work and pay structures. We all need to be advocates of justice, but as with many things, change starts with ourselves. Self-advocacy helps you speak up for what you value and express your thoughts, feelings, and needs to others. Self-advocacy empowers you to live more aligned with your values and ethics, and you will be able to regain a sense of freedom and authority over your own life. Self-advocacy will reveal what you can expect from others. And self-advocacy will not only improve the chances that you are being heard, even if the outcome is not what you wanted, but you will also feel better about yourself for having done so.

Reflection: Can you recall a time when you felt powerless to resolve a problem at work or in your profession, but at the same time felt that the responsibility for addressing the problem was being dumped on you? If so, describe what happened, how you felt, and what you did—or wanted to do—to address the problem.

_____

_____

_____

_____

_____

_____

_____

_____

Contemplation: Do you feel your social status, gender or ethnicity has suppressed your voice in any way? If so, how?

_____

_____

_____

_____

_____

_____

Contemplation: Where do you feel you need to use your voice more? Do you feel safe to do so? If not, what do you feel might happen if you did speak up?

_____

_____

_____

_____

_____

Step Forward: How can you use your voice to meet your needs this week? Think of one small step you can take or change you can make.

_____

_____

_____

_____

_____

_____

_____

_____

_____

Step Forward: If you do not feel safe speaking up about a concern at work, such as discrimination, harassment, a colleague's misconduct, or something else that could lead to retaliation, how can you speak directly to the person causing the problem, without further escalating the problem?

_____

_____

_____

_____

_____

_____

_____

_____

_____

_____

Step Forward: What specific things come to your mind that you would like to advocate for, that can lead to positive changes in the healthcare culture?

_____

_____

_____

_____

_____

_____

_____

_____

_____

Step Forward: Consider ways you might unite with your colleagues as one undivided voice to promote changes in the healthcare system that would benefit you, your profession, and your patients. If you felt safe to do so, what would you do? What are some of the issues you would address and how?

_____

_____

_____

_____

_____

_____

_____

_____

_____

_____

Step Forward: What's one *small* step you can take, or change you can make, toward making that happen?

_____

_____

_____

_____

_____

_____

_____

_____

_____

_____

***

I learned a long time ago that the wisest thing I can do is be on my own side and advocate for myself and others like me.

Dr. Maya Angelou

***

Trusting Your Gut

Medicine teaches us how to live inside our minds and be logical about everything. We are taught that medicine is a science that only requires brains and high grades. After the competition of medical schools, we live in the constant performance comparison of metrics and patient satisfaction scores. Health insurance companies and the health system profile us based on metrics, reviews, and expenditures. We are wired to compete and kill. In this "survival of the fittest," we live in our minds and suppress our guts, as we learn to ignore our instincts and pay attention only to the data. We learn that looking at the data and knowing all the differential diagnoses will protect us from the fears of failures and mistakes. Data and documentation will also save us from the dreaded lawsuit, we are taught, so we learn to go along.

The future does not appear to be addressing this problem, but instead, exacerbating it as Artificial Intelligence (AI) gains prominence in the medical industry. While AI has produced amazing achievements in diagnosis and surgical intervention, this technology has come at a cost. If machines and technology can provide better care than humans, some fear the physician-patient relationship may soon disappear altogether!

In the process of grappling with the rapid technological innovations (and invasions) into our profession, we forget our second brain, the mysterious enteric nervous system. The gut goes beyond the thoughts of our mind, and this intuition helps connect the brain, mind, emotions, and body. Listening to our bodies can genuinely reveal how we feel about specific situations or issues. Our bodies know and recognize danger.

Contemplation: What do you feel in your body when something is not right? What parts of your body become activated? How does your energy shift?

_____

_____

_____

_____

_____

_____

_____

Create! Can you draw how your body feels when you sense that something is not right? Don't worry about how well you can draw—have fun with it!

Create! Can you draw how your body feels when something *does* feel right?

Step Forward: How can you remind yourself to trust your gut when making patient-related decisions, decisions about your career (such as which jobs to accept and which to decline), and decisions about your personal life? What are some ways you can recognize what your gut is telling you in these pivotal moments?

_____

_____

_____

_____

_____

_____

_____

_____

_____

Reflection: Have you ever had an experience where your gut told you one thing, but your medical training, your supervising physician, or the health insurer, had you do another? How did you feel, and how did the situation turn out?

_____

_____

_____

_____

_____

_____

_____

Reflection: We all have patients who insist that they know what's wrong with them, and they can be impossible to care for when they ignore our advice. But have you ever had a patient who told you they just knew in their gut that something was wrong, and they turned out to be right? If so, what happened, and did that experience change the way you respond to your patients' "gut feelings?" How do you weigh balancing their "instincts" with their lack of medical knowledge?

_____

_____

_____

_____

_____

_____

_____

_____

Controlling and Acknowledging Your Emotions

In their book, *Empathy in Healthcare,* authors Ageliki Kerasidou, and Ruth Horn write, "The expression of emotions in medical practice is perceived as unprofessional, and many doctors learn to suppress and ignore their feelings. When facing stressful situations, these physicians are more likely to suffer from depression and burnout than those who engage with and reflect on their feelings."

Contemplation: What feelings and thoughts come up when you read this quote? Does it reflect how you relate to your emotions? Have you crafted methods to express and share feelings with your patients and colleagues? If so, what are these methods?

_____

_____

_____

_____

_____

_____

_____

_____

Contemplation: Do you feel safe sharing your feelings with colleagues and/or with patients? If not, would you feel safer doing so with a good friend, even if that friend might not understand your concerns as well as a colleague, or even a patient? What do you need in your relationships so that you feel safe sharing your feelings?

_____

_____

_____

_____

_____

_____

_____

_____

Trauma leads to either rigidity or chaos in our lives. In finding the dance of grace, we reconnect with ourselves and others' pain and suffering. Medical education and culture continue in many ways to perpetuate medical stoicism. We are taught to become indifferent to our emotions and the emotions of our patients.

Step Forward: How can you create more space to process your emotions? What do you need—in your mind, your relationships, or your environment— to allow yourself the space to explore your emotions? What steps can you take to create that space?

_____

_____

_____

_____

_____

_____

_____

_____

_____

_____

We have all had emotions that, at times, are too strong for us to handle. Instead, they rule over us and become masters that dictate our actions. Emotions that are a response to a sense of loss of control or a defense to our feeling attacked tend to result in what society calls "negative" emotions. As we learn to listen to these feelings, we can hear these emotions whispering to us. We can sense our bodies going from a state of calmness and control to a state of high activation. As we deal with conflict in our profession, energy will arise in parts of our body that scream *take action now!* But the actions we take when in a state of hyperarousal are not always constructive actions. Screaming, yelling, threatening, or storming off can kill our careers. Reporting injustices can do the same. These urges are not necessarily our thinking brain at work—they are the cry of our soul telling us something is not right—they are neither good nor bad. It's important to heed our emotions, but not let them control us. At times, attending to our bodies first allows for better response from our prefrontal cortex. By calming the body, we calm the mind. By calming the mind, we regain control. Regaining control allows us to attend to our soul with kindness without fighting the world, and without blaming the world, but rather by moving into change.

Step Forward: When you feel activated by your emotions, how can you give your body time to process your response? What things can you do at work to restore calmness in your body?

_____

_____

_____

_____

_____

_____

_____

_____

_____

_____

When we *react* to something, our primal state dominates. We tend to lash out, act impulsively, or flee. But when we *respond* to something, we assess the risks, consider our options, and address the problem.

Contemplation: Are you a responder or a reactor? If you are a responder, how do you avoid reacting? If you are a reactor, what steps can you take to respond more and react less?

_____

_____

_____

_____

_____

_____

_____

_____

One of the most primal emotions is anger. A quick Google search on physicians' anger reveals the many programs that have been developed to teach physicians how to manage this emotion and not be disruptive. Anger is an emotion that is neither good nor bad. Like other emotions, anger is an emotional reaction that can be constructive or destructive. Many physicians experience anger toward a system that continues to minimize our needs and concerns for our patients. Many physicians continue to feel devalued. Administrators increasingly promise "express and convenient" care. Others tell the stories of how their companies provide them with a mere ten minutes to see a patient. In some cases, a clicker is used to track time, and if a patient requires more than the allotted ten minutes, you need to choose between being financially penalized for spending time with the patient or not providing adequate care. Companies are increasingly hiring more mid-levels because "they are better for the business," pushing more physicians into supervising positions where they may not be able to choose who works under their licenses. We are considered elite professionals with exceptional skills and educations and high incomes (along with the high debt of our educations), yet we have no control or voice over our schedules, late shows, patient dismissals from the practice, or the clinic workflow. Anger speaks to us and provides us with the energy to move toward change. Anger also gnaws away at us, turning some of us bitter and resentful. We must learn to harness our anger toward constructive change.

***

Anger is a protest; it moves us toward justice.
Karen Rellos

***

Contemplation: What injustices do you perceive in our current healthcare system? How about the workplace? Who is affected by these injustices?

_____

_____

_____

_____

_____

_____

_____

_____

_____

Contemplation: What emotions and thoughts do these injustices awaken in you?

_____

_____

_____

_____

_____

_____

_____

_____

Contemplation: What changes in the healthcare system make you the angriest?

_____

_____

_____

_____

_____

_____

_____

Contemplation: What is your anger screaming? Write it down. Now say it out loud.

_____

_____

_____

_____

_____

_____

_____

Step Forward: What actions do you feel you need to take to quell your anger? Remember, we are not victims, and we always have the power to move in one direction or the other. We do not need to tolerate injustice to survive.

_____

_____

_____

_____

_____

_____

_____

_____

_____

_____

If anger is not expressed and is stored in our bodies, it only leads to decay. Anger, like other emotions, needs to be processed. An external outburst of anger can liberate your body while creating further problems for you to navigate. Or it can be expressed constructively, such as throwing a basketball at a wall or hitting a tennis ball hard across the court. Anger is an emotion we need to learn to manage.

Step Forward: What can you do when you become angry in the workplace? How can you suppress the instinct to lash out, while not denying your anger or any injustice or bad behavior you perceive?

_____

_____

_____

_____

_____

_____

_____

_____

_____

_____

Step Forward: How can you creatively express your anger, in healthy ways, outside the office? Punching bag ... tossing a medicine ball against the wall repeatedly ... breaking some glass .... Think outside the box. List some strategies for expressing your anger.

_____

_____

_____

_____

_____

_____

_____

_____

_____

_____

***

Underneath anger is pain, your pain...Anger is strength, and it can be an anchor giving temporary structure to the nothingness of loss.

Elisabeth Kubler Ross

***

Transforming Shame

Another powerful emotion we often feel is shame. As doctors, we are trained to feel pride. Yet for many of us, our pride conceals our inner shame. Physicians are exposed to shaming experiences daily. Shame is closely connected to blame—when we feel blamed, we tend to feel ashamed, thinking something is our fault and therefore we are bad. Every time a patient complains, feelings of shame and humiliation may creep in, leading us to wonder if we really did do something wrong. This sense of shame is exacerbated by perfectionism—feeling we need to be perfect in order to be worthy. Yet perfectionism is impossible to achieve in medicine, just as it is impossible to achieve in life. The more we embrace the perfectionism that has been instilled in us in medical school, the more shame we are likely to experience when we fall short—thus increasing our risk of mental health disorders.

Shame is a feeling of being less than others, having a secret we dare not let others know. This secret is that we feel we do not belong in our profession, something known as "Imposter Syndrome." Imposter Syndrome is especially common to women, people of color, people from working-class backgrounds, and members of the LBGTQ community. Physicians from these groups have often been raised to believe they were inferior, and to feel shame in who they are. As they overcome the odds and rise to the highly-respected social class of physicians, they fear being exposed as unworthy of their profession—regardless of how hard they've worked, how much they've accomplished, or how skilled and intelligent they are.

Perhaps you feel a sense of "Imposter Syndrome." If so, you may be hypersensitive to rejection, become a social exile, and judge yourself harshly, even when others praise you. This can look like many things, but

I believe part of what makes it worst for a physician is the message we receive from different voices that makes us think we're invisible. We risk and then experience failure without repair, connection, or joy. We turn against ourselves when we discover we are vincible. To be seen and heal our shame, we must embrace the humility that will lead to vulnerability. Medicine is an imperfect and long journey that will have stories of failure. For physicians, that failure can include being involved in a medical malpractice lawsuit. A medical malpractice lawsuit is one of the events that cause extreme trauma response and shame to physicians. It is a perfect example of taboo talk because many feel ashamed. Other sources of shame may be a less-than-glowing review, being passed up for a raise or promotion, or being bullied or mobbed, as we've discussed previously.

Contemplation: Can you remember an experience in your medical career that produced shame and, as a result, you turned against yourself? What happened?

_____

_____

_____

_____

_____

_____

_____

Contemplation: Why do you think failure, for many physicians, provokes shame that leads to silence?

_____

_____

_____

_____

_____

_____

_____

_____

Contemplation: What are your thoughts on medical errors? Do you think it is inevitable to one day every physician will make one? If you do make a mistake or have made a mistake, does it mean you are deserving of shame?

_____

_____

_____

_____

_____

_____

_____

_____

Step Forward: One of the symptoms of Imposter Syndrome is disengaging from society, and withdrawing from interactions with colleagues because you feel you don't fit in. Have you had that experience? If so, how can you engage in a safe community that will welcome your vulnerability, while at the same time seeing you and offering you joy? If not, have you noticed any colleagues doing so? Can you think of ways you might be more inviting and encourage them to your community?

_____

_____

_____

_____

_____

_____

_____

_____

_____

_____

Many physicians have expressed feelings of shame because they feel unable to provide adequate care to their patients for reasons beyond their control. The COVID-19 pandemic has been just one of the reasons these feelings have exploded. As physicians tried to address the shortcomings of the healthcare system that interfered with, or prevented, their care to patients during the pandemic, many administrators used COVID-19 as the scapegoat of an already dysfunctional system, blaming the problem solely on the pandemic, while ignoring the problems of our healthcare system on dealing with the pandemic.

Contemplation: What other scapegoats do you perceive the health system embraces to deny its dysfunction? In what ways have you felt you couldn't provide the patient care you wanted to provide because the current healthcare system was dysfunctional, yet you or something else were blamed for that dysfunction?

_____

_____

_____

_____

_____

_____

_____

_____

Step Forward: Are there any actions you can take to bring such scapegoating to light? If you felt safe to do so, what would you like to do or say to improve our healthcare system so that you could provide better patient care?

_____

_____

_____

_____

_____

_____

_____

_____

_____

Step Forward: As our daily work has become increasingly dependent on technology, there is less space for connectedness, for clinicians to come together to play, have fun, train, and reflect. This isolation makes the voice of shame louder even as it speaks its lies. How can you help create a no-blame, learning, fair culture in medicine/in our workplaces?

_____

_____

_____

_____

_____

Notes

PART THREE

Post-Traumatic Growth

Improved
Relationships

New
Possibilities

Greater
Appreciation
of Life

Personal
Strength

Spiritual
Change

Regaining Your Humanity

Trauma affects how we see ourselves, our world, and the future. Traumatic events fragment us into many pieces, affecting our emotions and personality. After trauma, our brains continually look for danger, whether real or perceived, and we become hypersensitive to any potential threat. We avoid the danger in a myriad of ways, withholding parts of ourselves to avoid getting hurt again. We create a false self in this dance, and negative narratives form as realities to navigate this world. We make sacrifices that cost us our health and relationships and separate us from our hearts. We adapt to survive. We do what we need to do until we find a safe space for our wounded parts.

It's a dance I know well. I was not your typical medical student in the library or the coffee shop, studying like there was no other purpose in life. I knew that to learn, I needed to be mentally strong. Fortunately, I completed my medical school on the small and amazing island of Puerto Rico. Many days, I would take the bus to the beach and study there for hours. Earth has always been my monastery. The sounds of the waves, the breeze caressing my hair and body, the warm shining sun, and the contrasting colors of nature helped me to focus and study. Sadly, I had to leave the beauty of the mountains and waves of the ocean to complete my residency. After moving to rural Pennsylvania, it soon became apparent that I did not quite fit in this new and alien environment.

Changes were needed if I did not want to feel rejected. As a Puerto Rican woman, I talk fast and loudly. We naturally keep less social distance when talking with someone, and touching is habitual. Everybody hugs or stretches their arm on the island. I also loved the colors of the island, the brilliant greens of the mountains, the blues of the ocean, and the rainbow of our many flowers. These were the colors I wore each day. But it wasn't long before I became conscious of sticking out, especially as I was not a white American. I wanted to fit in, and I wanted to succeed, so I tucked the spunk into a small pocket of my life. I bought clothes in "professional colors" which meant black, grey, white, dark blue, and brown, gave up the flashy jewelry, and did my best to blend in so that I didn't stand out.

I even started to keep my distance from people and sit on my hands to avoid touching anyone. I changed. I became another person because I wanted to graduate from residency. I felt professionalism meant "whiteness," and I did not fit this definition. The transformation was insidious, as I began to see myself as a "professional," without realizing how much of my core self I had sacrificed.

One fall, my mom came to visit from Puerto Rico. I would leave for work as she entertained herself in the small apartment I rented. She would cook, clean, and buy all the things a mom feels her daughter needs to set up her new home. Returning from work one day I was happy to see that she had done all my laundry and placed everything in the closet. I thanked her but was startled by her reply. "When did you start to dress in these colors?" she asked me with disapproval. I became frozen and provided no response. I suddenly realized that I had become someone my own mother didn't recognize. I had to find myself again.

Whomever it was that you were when you began your medical career, it's likely you have changed. In some ways, these changes have been constructive. Maturity, new insights, and exposure to new people, experiences, and ideas, help us to become multifaceted, interesting people. But in other ways, these changes often take us from our true nature. Your true nature is your humanity. Claim it!

Contemplation: In what ways have you changed from your core self to someone you don't always recognize?

_____

_____

_____

_____

_____

_____

_____

Contemplation: How does professionalism look to you? How does unprofessionalism look?

_____

_____

_____

_____

_____

_____

_____

Reflection: In what ways did you adjust to fit the "medical professional identity" during your training? Think how you shifted internally during medical school, residency, fellowship, and practicing physician. In what ways have you changed toward a better version of yourself, and in what ways do you feel you have drifted from your core Self?

_____

_____

_____

_____

_____

_____

_____

Reflection: Did you ever feel your "medical professional identity" was challenged due to your race, ethnicity, sex, sexual orientation, or spiritual beliefs? If so, in what ways were you challenged? Did these challenges make

you a better doctor, or undermine your confidence and your work even
more difficult?

_____

_____

_____

_____

_____

_____

_____

Contemplation: What does being authentic mean to you? Do you feel
medicine has wounded your humanity? If so, in what ways? Has it made you
feel more fully human in any way? How so?

_____

_____

_____

_____

_____

_____

_____

Step Forward: Imagine the authentic self you hope to be. What does
that person look like? What are their character traits and strengths? What

motivates them—what is it that they strive for? Describe that person who is the true you.

_____

_____

_____

_____

_____

_____

_____

_____

_____

Sometimes change can be good, and sometimes change moves us far from who we were initially. Traumatic experiences create broken memories, smaller pieces that are hard to put together. You might not find words to express yourself, and time becomes wasted as we start to dissociate. We separate the part of us that has suffered harm from the other parts of ourselves. We alienate the trauma from the good things that life has to offer. We develop different behaviors to escape fragmentation and dissociation. Anything that will remove us from the reality of our pain.

This breaking and escaping can lead to emotional detachment, forgetting events, separating yourself from the world around you, and poor attuning to your own emotions. Your body, feelings, and mind are in a compartment, working separately to survive with no connection.

I hadn't realized how much I had changed since becoming a physician until the pandemic hit. COVID shifted me and brought me back to the things I loved and kept me alive. I began dancing and participating in Nia classes, which are high-intensity dance movements based on martial arts, dance, and healing. I had not danced since my first year of medical school. Who had time for professional dancing in med school? I also learned to relax. I bought myself a hammock and created a small garden. The hammock and the breeze took me back to the sweet memories of Puerto Rico. I have added colorful decorations to my office and even a Curious George toy! And I have educated myself beyond medical school to practice holistically and empower my patients to regain their health naturally and gently. I am moving back toward my initial vision behind attending medical school, what many call the integration of medicine and wellness. I am finding myself again—and as I do, I discover that I'm becoming a better physician, with more energy, more compassion, and more focus.

Regaining your humanity means finding the pieces of your Self that have been discarded or fragmented with time. Instead of mourning their loss, welcome the return of these many parts and pieces that have been discarded or fragmented with time. As you integrate these parts, you become more fully alive.

Step Forward: What are some qualities of your professional identity that you want to keep as you move forward in a new way of living?

_____

_____

_____

_____

_____

_____

_____

What are some qualities that you want to leave behind because they do not feel authentic to your true Self?

_____

_____

_____

_____

_____

_____

Reflection: What hobbies or activities did you abandon because medicine absorbed all your time and energy?

_____

_____

_____

_____

_____

_____

_____

_____

_____

Step Forward: Looking at the above list, can you think of any ways you might return to one or more of these activities to bring more joy into your life?

_____

_____

_____

_____

_____

Create! Can you draw yourself with a "new" professional identity that shows your uniqueness and beauty? Don't worry about how well you can draw, have fun with it!

***

If you are divided from your body, you are also divided from the body of the world, which then appears to be other than you or separate from you, rather than the living continuum to which you belong.
Philip Shepherd, author of New Self, New World

***

Creating New Communities

I have heard many physicians talk about how they lost their tribe after residency. You are now in a job that demands you to go from room to room, speaking only to a medical assistant or nurse to give orders about what needs to be done. You might connect with some patients at a human level, but usually, there is no time for this. You do not have time to speak with your colleagues about patient care or life in general. You interact with a parade of people every day, yet you might feel lonely at work because none of these connections are personal ones. Then you leave work, go home to work a couple of extra hours to finish charting and answer patient messages and requests. Your energy is stolen by a system that somehow concludes that one person can care for over two thousand people. It's an impossible goal that no physician can ever reach, no matter how hard we work. That's why you need a community to connect to, a community that shares your concerns, your values, and your interests.

Creating community requires being vulnerable, however. Vulnerability is an antidote to all the negative sequela in our minds about ourselves once we have experience traumatic events. Vulnerability will open the doors to community and lift the burden of the events as you discover you are not alone.

Contemplation: How do you feel vulnerable as a doctor? How might sharing your stories of vulnerability in medicine help your professional community?

_____

_____

_____

_____

_____

_____

_____

_____

Reflection: What do you do, or refrain from doing, to protect yourself from this vulnerability?

_____

_____

_____

_____

_____

_____

_____

_____

Reflection: Reflect on your answers above and consider whether your efforts at self-protection are enhancing your life or limiting it. In what ways might you take more risks, embracing your vulnerability while moving toward more supportive communities?

_____

_____

_____

_____

_____

_____

_____

Step Forward: Given the limited time you have each day; how can you create more meaningful relationships with your colleagues?

_____

_____

_____

_____

_____

_____

_____

_____

Step Forward: Perhaps you have felt you do not fit in due to your race, gender, spiritual beliefs, values, style of practice, culture, or personality. Can you think of ways of finding a new tribe of doctors who will embrace you?

_____

_____

_____

_____

_____

_____

_____

_____

_____

***

Of all the things trauma takes away from us, the worst is our willingness, or even our ability, to be vulnerable. There's a reclaiming that has to happen.

Brené Brown, Rising Strong: The Reckoning. The Rumble. The Revolution

***

You're Grounded!

When we were kids, being grounded was the last thing that we wanted. It meant we were stuck inside while our friends were out having fun. Now that we're adults, however, being grounded has an entirely different meaning. To be grounded means to be centered, fully present, and in tune with the earth beneath us, and the infinite sky above us. Let's start here, with a simple reflection to help you reach that grounded center.

I've chosen two approaches to grounding yourself, and both work well. Choose the one that most speaks to you or try them both to find the right fit. Start by being seated and comfortable as you release the tension in your body—relax your face, unclench your teeth, and let your shoulders fall. Sink into the earth. Are your hands clutching the arms of the chair? Relax them. Are your legs shaking, your feet lifting from the floor? Set your feet softly on the floor to ground yourself to the earth.

Step Forward: Become grounded in the present moment using your breath. Deep breathing relieves stress and helps us to relax. Our breath helps calm our nervous system. It also activates the parasympathetic nervous system, allowing us to return to the here and now. Attend to your body via your breath. Calm your mind and body down by focused breathing. Set a timer. Start with slow, steady, and deep breaths for one minute and slowly increase to three minutes. Breathe in for a count of four to six. Hold for a second, then exhale for a count of six to eight. Place one hand on your belly and another on your heart, and breathe deeply again, feeling your belly expand with each breath and feeling the rhythmic beating of your heart. If it helps, imagine your belly like a balloon filling as you inhale, deflating as you exhale.

Repeat until your timer alerts you to breathe normally again. Feel the tension dissipate as your parasympathetic nervous system relaxes.

_____

_____

_____

_____

_____

_____

_____

_____

_____

_____

Step Forward: Become grounded in the present by using your senses. Using our senses when we feel disengaged, not present in the moment, or overwhelmed by events will help the mind return to the present which shifts our nervous system. After reading this paragraph, close your eyes. What do you hear? Listen for the sounds of the wind, the creaks of your house, a distant car, a bird chirping in a distant tree. How many different sounds can you discern? Moving to your nose, what do you smell? Inhale deeply, exhale, and inhale again. Can you smell flowers, freshly mowed grass, or your own body odor? Don't judge the smells, just smell them. Try to identify at least two smells, whether scents or odors. Now taste your own tongue. Can you taste your morning coffee? The tea or wine you just sipped? The toothpaste lingering in your mouth? Now feel your tongue, let it glide over your hard palate, the back of your hard teeth. Feel the chair you sit upon, the floor beneath your feet, the book you hold in your hands. Feel everything that touches you. Now open your eyes. What do you see? Note every color, every texture, every object in your sight. The flicker of a burning candle. A window to the world outside, a tender plant. Breathe deeply. You are here. In the Now. What better place to be?

_____

_____

_____

_____

_____

_____

_____

_____

_____

_____

The Five Senses

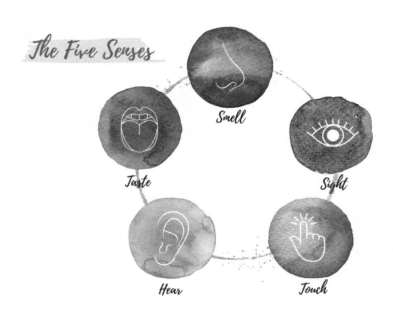

Smell

Sight

Taste

Touch

Hear

The healing journey can mean white-knuckling all the way, or it can be a delicate and slow process of self-discovery and reflection. I invite you to embrace the gift of time, curiosity, acceptance, and compassion as you evolve and reinvent yourself professionally. Your healing begins with taking the pressure off, but before you can do that, you must identify where and how you feel pressured.

Contemplation: In what ways do you feel pressured in your personal and professional life?

_____

_____

_____

_____

_____

_____

_____

Step Forward: List some of the things you can outsource by hiring someone to do them or delegating to someone else, as well as things you can do later, or relinquish altogether. What would it mean to not get it all done?

_____

_____

_____

_____

_____

_____

_____

_____

_____

_____

Step Forward: What is the kindest thing you can do for yourself this week?

_____

_____

_____

_____

_____

_____

_____

_____

_____

***

Love does not demand. Love always gifts kindness.

***

Selfcare

Self-care is essential, though it won't change the brokenness of our healthcare system. But caring for yourself will make you stronger and provide you with resources to move into a better life. Some quick tips in the office that have worked for me: fresh fruits are my snack to go; I always keep essential oils in my drawer; I have flowers or a plant in my office to bring life and growth into my workspace; a short walk at lunchtime gives me a break from my computer, sitting and office space; I don't multitask, I check work emails only once a day; and I finish my notes at work so that I when I go home at the end of the day, my workday is done. Focusing on self-care and our own well-being makes us better doctors and better people. Think about ways you can incorporate self-care into your daily—and nightly—routine, getting the rest you need, and destressing throughout the day.

Contemplation: How important and attainable is sleep for you?

_____

_____

_____

_____

_____

_____

_____

_____

Step Forward: How can you create more space for rest and just be?

_____

_____

_____

_____

_____

_____

_____

_____

Contemplation: When you hear the word de-stress, what comes to mind?

_____

_____

_____

_____

_____

_____

_____

Reflection: What makes your day stressful and are any of those things under your control?

_____

_____

_____

_____

_____

_____

_____

_____

Often when we try to alleviate our stress, we seek immediate relief. And while deep breathing techniques can be a particularly healthy way to destress quickly, instantaneous efforts to relieve stress are often unhealthy. Self-medicating through licit or illicit drugs, alcohol abuse, unsafe or risky sex (such as sexual addiction or infidelity), or computer or TV addiction, are all ways in which we seek to escape but create new problems as we do so. These are forms of short-term adaptation to stress, but in the long term, they're maladaptive as they lead to more problems. One of the most common forms of unhealthy destressing is through food. That is because as children, we learn to de-stress through our bodies—by "acting out," playing, screaming, jumping, running, or eating something comforting. That is why sex and food can become so problematic for adults who have survived trauma.

Food should not be a source of stress, although it can become in many ways yet one more source of stress because we have learned since childhood to self-regulate and soothe our bodies with food—perhaps you eat too much, deprive yourself of too much, or eat fast or processed food on the run, paying no attention as you eat while you drive or fill out paperwork. Think about food as a source of nourishment, and nourishment is not only about food, but about all the many ways you nourish and care for your body. How do you love to nourish your body? List all the ways you nourish your body inside and out.

Create! Can you draw and color what the perfect meal, looks like for you? Look at this picture, what do you see?

Nourish

20%
Whole Grains

10%
Nuts, Seeds & Avocado

20%
Plant-based Protein

50%
Whole Fruits & Vegetables

"Let food be thy medicine."

Reflection: How many fruits and vegetables did your picture include? If you don't include many fruits and vegetables in your meal, why is that?

_____

_____

_____

_____

_____

_____

_____

Does your perfect meal include spices and herbs? Why or why not?

_____

_____

_____

_____

_____

_____

_____

Does your eating reflect the colors of the rainbow? If not, how could you include more color into your meal?

_____

_____

_____

_____

_____

_____

_____

_____

The meals we eat aren't just about nourishing our bodies—they nourish our souls, as well, by providing a communal ritual where relationships are fostered and healed. We are wounded in relationships; we are also healed in relationships. Many physicians feel they lack a sense of community in their work; we work around people all day but may still feel lonely. There are many sources of community, other doctors like you, social media groups, faith-based groups, sports, or other hobbies-related groups. We all need a tribe that flourishes and supports us. One way we can imagine this sense of intimacy and community is by the image of gathering together at the table to enjoy a meal, plan a project, or just engage in a lively conversation.

Create! Can you draw and color what comes to mind when you hear "come to the table?"

Another element of self-care is playful movement. In his book, *Keep Moving,* comedian and actor Dick Van Dyke talks about the importance of play, urging readers to dance and sing and engage the child within every day.

Reflection: What was your favorite game growing up? What did you most enjoy about it?

_____

_____

_____

_____

_____

_____

_____

_____

Reflection: What did you do as a child that always brought you a smile? What was it that brought you happiness?

_____

_____

_____

_____

_____

_____

_____

_____

Think about ways you can bring more beauty into your life. Humans are the only species capable of appreciating aesthetics. Our brains have evolved to give meaning to visual balance, shape, color, and patterns without a need for function. Beauty thus provides us with a sense of appreciation and inner calm.

Contemplation: Do you believe exposing yourself to beauty can work as a catharsis to move you towards healing and true self? How would more beauty in your life help you to heal?

_____

_____

_____

_____

_____

_____

_____

_____

Step Forward: What people, animals, places, and things inspire you? Can you create space in your life to walk briefly in nature and exposed yourself to the sun, the wind, and the stars? How might you do that to bring more natural beauty to your life?

_____

_____

_____

_____

_____

_____

_____

_____

_____

_____

Finally, I want you to think about gratitude as a form of self-care. Gratitude can serve as your "happy" hormone. When we give and receive gratitude our dopamine and serotonin levels increase. We feel good. Close your eyes for a moment, take a deep breath and hold for three seconds, then slowly exhale. As you do so, picture all you are grateful for, the truly important things in your life. Write down ten things you are grateful for in your life.

Somatic Embodiment

We inscribe our stress onto our bodies in a multitude of ways. High blood pressure, GI issues, headaches, eating disorders, teeth clenching, tense muscles, lowered immunity, and even serious diseases, are among the many ways we embody our stress. For this reason, I invite you to attend to your body, so that you can better understand that different situations can provoke sensations in your body, and these sensations can lead you to live outside your window of tolerance. When this happens, we perpetuate an unhealthy cycle, as our stress defines our bodies, our bodies become a source of greater stress, which creates more somatic problems. Whether through unhealthy eating, substance abuse, immune disorders, or tension in our bones and muscles, this cycle can feel like an impossible cycle to break. But the cycle can be broken, once you have gained awareness of what is feeding it.

Deep breathing exercises are excellent for immediate stress relief. Research on biofeedback has shown that we can slow our own heart rate just through concentration. And "power posing" – making an A with your body by standing with feet apart at shoulder width, arms outstretched in the V for victory position—can give us instant confidence if we stand like that for just twenty seconds. Body scans to relax our muscles from head to toe, simple stretches, and even just smiling in the mirror for a minute or two, can alleviate stress, depression, and anxiety. And we know well how effective exercise, dance, walking, swimming, and other forms of body movement can have long-term positive effects on our emotions and moods. By becoming more aware of the connections between our psychology and our physiology, we can make great changes.

Contemplation: Imagine your body moving freely through space, feeling the cooling sensation of the sky caressing your skin, the wind massaging your muscles, and the sunshine warming your face. Describe this experience of floating through the sky, free of any pain or tension. How does each body part feel as it moves without effort or intent? How does your mind perceive the experience?

_____

_____

_____

_____

_____

_____

_____

_____

Reflection: When you have had a difficult day, how does your body feel? During a tense confrontation with a colleague, a difficult conversation with a patient, or a stern rebuke from a supervisor or other doctor, how does your body tense up? Do you prepare for fight or flight by clenching your fists, firming your stance, or becoming more rigid? Does your jaw clench, your face tighten, or your stomach churn? Reflect on a difficult moment at work and how your body felt. Do you feel those same feelings returning as you recall the event? Write them down. When you're done, imagine the memory dissolving and your body relaxing. Describe the sensations you feel as the memory dissolves.

_____

_____

_____

_____

_____

_____

_____

_____

Step Forward: List five things you can do to relax in the moment—such as taking deep breaths, focusing on your heart rate as you feel it slow down, or simply stretching—when you are in a high-stress situation and five things you can do when you are not working to ease into your body and give it the care and attention it deserves.

_____

_____

_____

_____

_____

_____

_____

_____

_____

_____

When I am in a high-stress situation at work and need to instantly relax, I can: _____

_____.

Now list five things you can do outside of work that will involve your body—whether that's various forms of exercise, housework, gardening, or other daily activities. Make these things that you can enjoy, not more work you have to do.

_____

_____

_____

_____

_____

_____

_____

_____

_____

When I come home from work, I can move my body through: _____

_____.

Seeking Stability

Have you ever felt like you are on a rollercoaster ride as you go from peace to fear in your career, or sometimes just your day? Perhaps you vacillate, not sure if you should do something or stay the course, choose one option or another, for fear of making the wrong choice. Should you stay in this job, or go after another? Should you expand to this specialty or that one? Should you get trained in a new diagnostic technique, or stick with what you've been doing? Prescribe this treatment or that one? Uncertainty and indecision can be incredibly stressful. Your amygdala activates when you do not feel in control. For many of us, our medical career started with uncomfortable shifts. One school for undergraduate, another state for medical school, then we move yet again for the residency program, and then we navigate to new horizons as a young physicians. And because becoming a physician tends to coincide with the life stage when most of us marry and have children, we live in a constant state of change and uncertainty. All these changes create rapid inner movement. Medicine molds us to tolerate unpredictability. But creating some routine and predictability will help reduce these feelings of uncertainty and improve the daily quality of your life.

Reflection: Have you had to move and leave the comfort of your community behind to pursue your medical career? How did that move feel beforehand? Were you excited, anxious, or some other feeling? Once you made the move, how did you feel? If so, in what ways? Feel free to discuss the multiple moves you've made and how those moves have shaped you and changed your life.

_____

_____

_____

_____

_____

_____

_____

_____

Reflection: How did moving for your career impact your relationships and finances?

_____

_____

_____

_____

_____

_____

_____

Reflection: Did all these changes create feelings of uncertainty? If so, do you remember how you handled it?

_____

_____

_____

_____

_____

_____

Step Forward: How have you maintained a sense of stability amidst the moves you've made? Describe some ways you've created a sense of security and stability throughout your medical career.

_____

_____

_____

_____

_____

_____

_____

_____

_____

Contemplation: Do you worry about having to move again for your career, or for another reason that might affect your career? If so, what are some of your fears, and how might you alleviate those fears?

_____

_____

_____

_____

_____

_____

_____

_____

A lack of stability in our lives can trigger feelings of fear about the future. Living with instability keeps us in a constant state of uncertainty, and we feel as if we have little control over our own lives. The medical profession is fraught with these feelings, even if we are settled in a job and home and family life. If we make a mistake, everything could collapse. We are dependent on our employers for our stability. If we don't work hard enough, we could lose our jobs. If we don't spend more time with our families, we could end up divorced. If we aren't married, we could end up alone because we work too hard. These feelings of uncertainty, fear, and lack of control keep our amygdala constantly activated, resulting in a constant state of anxiety. At the heart of this anxiety, is a sense of not having control. Gaining control over our lives reduces the anxiety.

Step Forward: What are some important things you feel are in your circle of control at your job and outside your job?

_____

_____

_____

_____

_____

_____

_____

_____

_____

What are some things you feel you are powerless to control and need to let go of?

To gain a sense of stability in our lives, our instinct is to gain control. But there are some things in our lives we cannot control, especially things that have already happened. When we cannot control something, we need to let go. Letting go does not mean you do not care or that it does not hurt. It means making a conscious decision to create space between you and X. It means detaching from the effects the issue has on us.

Contemplation: "Letting go" is not always as easy as saying we should do it. What are some things that make letting go difficult for you? What would it mean if you let some of these things go? What would it mean if you didn't? Look at the list above or reflect on some things you didn't put down because you feel you can't let them go. Choose a few to reflect on in the following lines:

If I let go of _____, it

would mean _____.

If I let go of _____, it

would mean _____.

If I let go of _____, it

would mean _____.

If I let go of _____, it

would mean _____.

If I let go of _____, it

would mean _____.

A lack of control or a sense of powerlessness is stressful because as physicians, we are accustomed to solving problems, which gives us a sense of control over our work. But we have little control over our day-to-day lives as our employers determine our work schedules, our patient loads, and even our treatment approaches. The control that many physicians feel is missing in medicine is related to our loss of autonomy to not only practice medicine but also over our schedules and our lives. Not having that control over our lives leaves us with a constant state of uncertainty.

Contemplation: What are some of the uncertainties that cause you stress? Can you list five of them?

_____

_____

_____

_____

_____

_____

_____

_____

_____

_____

Step Forward: Now think about how you might embrace the uncertainty of each of these things. For example, we are all uncertain about how and when we will die. Even someone with a terminal illness who thinks they know exactly what will kill them and approximately when they could die unexpectedly from something else. To embrace the uncertainty of death, we can embrace each day that we are alive, being thankful and observant of even the smallest gifts of our days. Suppose you listed among your uncertainties whether you're a good doctor. Maybe deep down you second guess your skills, wondering if you made the right choice in becoming a doctor. How might you embrace that uncertainty? You could acknowledge that you do have more to learn, and strive to learn something new each day, take more CME classes, and maybe even dip your toes into something outside of medicine altogether, to see if maybe you might one day venture into a whole new career. In this way, you are accepting that you do have uncertainties about your chosen profession, but that those uncertainties are okay—they propel you to gain more knowledge and open you to new and unexplored possibilities for the future.

_____

_____

_____

_____

_____

_____

_____

_____

_____

Step Forward: Read over the five uncertainties you listed above and think about how you might embrace them. As you do so, think about how knowledge/certainty are about control, while curiosity opens the way to new truths.

_____

_____

_____

_____

_____

_____

_____

_____

_____

_____

Step Forward: Now reflect on how you feel now that you have given some thought to how feelings of control, uncertainty, and powerlessness have shaped you, as well as how these feelings can be allies, and may even empower you in unexpected ways.

_____

_____

_____

_____

_____

_____

_____

_____

***

The quest for certainty blocks the search for meaning. Uncertainty is the very condition to impel man to unfold his powers.
Erich Fromm

***

Finding Joy

Regaining Your humanity means finding joy in your life. As children, joy comes naturally to us, but as we grow older, we lose that spontaneous sense of pure joy. Joy is more than a positive emotion. Joy is an internal state. Finding joy in the midst of circumstances beyond our control will reduce pain and illnesses while increasing your life span. Joy is bringing your body back to a state of delight and harmony. Joy says all is good and well. Joy brings us purpose in our work. Joy brings a smile to our faces and lightens our bodies and our days. We become more outgoing and engaged in this world because this sense of joy lightens and harmony. But no matter how naturally optimistic and happy you might be, it's easy to lose that sense of joy when you've been working fifteen-hour days, abused by colleagues and patients, watched a patient die, or told another their diagnosis is dire. Before long, we forget how joy even feels and the longer we don't feel it, the greater the struggle to regain it. That's why it's so important to take action and restore your sense of joy.

Contemplation: What or who consistently brings you joy?

_____

_____

_____

_____

_____

_____

_____

Reflection: When was the last time you felt pure joy? Were you alone or with someone else or others? Describe your joy and the events or setting that inspired your joy.

_____

_____

_____

_____

_____

_____

_____

_____

Contemplation: In what ways does being more filled with joy impact your physician-patient relationship?

_____

_____

_____

_____

_____

_____

_____

_____

Step Forward: How can you bring joy to your work and your patients?

_____

_____

_____

_____

_____

***

I can't die yet, doctor. Not yet. I have things to do. Afterward, I'll have a whole lifetime in which to die.

Carlos Ruiz Zafron

***

Faith

Our careers in medicine have given us a front-row seat to life and death, as we witness births, devastating injuries, debilitating diseases, and far too many deaths. We save lives and we ease our patients into gentle deaths wherever possible and necessary. We have been trained to intervene and cure sickness, heal wounds, and prevent deaths. And when we are unable to do so, we so often call on a power greater than our own to intervene in some remarkable way. Doing so isn't giving up. It is acknowledging that we are human and that our powers are limited.

For some of us, having a Higher Power keeps us going when we feel the waters rising as we swim through a storm. A Higher Power is something we hold on to and reach out to for strength, wisdom, and comfort. A Higher Power might be God in the Judeo-Christian sense, it might be Allah, it might be fate, or simply the Universe. Whatever this Higher Power might be for you, I have no doubt you have called on it in times of trouble.

Contemplation: Do you have a Higher Power? If yes, how have the experiences in medicine affected your relationship with your Higher Power and the beauty of this world? If not, in what ways have your healthcare experiences impacted how you view the world?

_____
_____
_____
_____
_____
_____

_____

_____

In our healing journey, we need something to hold on to while the flood waters recede. Having an anchor of hope is something that gives us the energy we need to keep going, whether it be our family, a vacation trip, retirement, or even our pets, who keep us going and anchor us in hope.

Step Forward: What is or can be your anchor and how can that anchor bring you hope when you feel overwhelmed?

_____

_____

_____

_____

_____

_____

_____

_____

_____

_____

Creativity

Medicine is both an art and a science, yet it's the scientific side of our profession that is most rewarded. In many respects, that makes sense—science has enabled us to treat and even prevent disease, heal wounds, perform miraculous surgeries, and given us the greatest technological advances ever known. But as our brains focus on this science, another part of our brains gets less exercise—our creative side, our ability to perceive patterns, imagine possibilities, and above all, to create. This creative side is especially important to healing from the stresses, abuses, and traumas of our profession.

Symbolisms and imagery can help the brain process and make sense of our trauma. Creative art can be a tool to empower our emotions and express visceral pain while containing the trauma. Expressive arts can help us develop grounding and coping skills that are much needed while on the journey of healing. To tap into this side of your brain and embark on this journey of healing, begin by thinking of yourself as a child.

Reflection: Can you remember when you had fun doing something out of the box? What did you do and how did it feel to do it?

_____

_____

_____

_____

_____

_____

Step Forward: How can you express your feelings with beauty and creativity? Do you have any artistic outlets, or have you considered developing some skills in these areas? What most inspires you? (If you feel resistant to expressing your creativity, consider developing it in small steps, such as buying a coloring book, taking an authentic movement class, or learning to draw or paint or play a musical instrument).

_____

_____

_____

_____

_____

_____

_____

_____

_____

Step Forward: Can you use expressive arts in your patient encounters? In what ways?

_____

_____

_____

_____

_____

_____

_____

_____

_____

_____

***

When you make music or write or create, it's really your job to have mind-blowing, irresponsible, condomless sex with whatever idea it is you're writing about at the time.

Lady Gaga

***

Self-Forgiveness

After a traumatic event, we often struggle with self-forgiveness because as physicians, we have a strong sense of responsibility. We blame ourselves when things go wrong, we beat ourselves up with could've/should've scripts that play in the back of our minds. We feel we must do everything, be everything, and take care of everything. Yet it's impossible to do all and be all, avoid mistakes, and make nothing but perfect decisions. Yes, we need to accept responsibility when it's called for, but we must also be as forgiving of ourselves as we are of others.

Reflection: Can you recall an event in your medical career that caused you shame and guilt? Be as descriptive as possible.

_____

_____

_____

_____

_____

_____

_____

Contemplation: Now think about the consequences of this event on your identity and worth. Write down all the negative statements swirling in your head because of this experience.

How did this experience separate you from your values and a positive sense of self?

_____

_____

_____

_____

_____

_____

_____

Step Forward: Now imagine that your child has been beating him or herself up with these same statements. Re-read them as if said by your child. If you don't have a child, think of a loved one, or a child you care about. What would you say to that child or loved one?

_____

_____

_____

_____

_____

_____

_____

_____

_____

Step Forward: Now imagine the child in you, your inner child, or even the innocent first-year medical student you once were. Speak these same words to your inner child. How does it feel to hear these words? Are you resistant to them? Why or why not? Can you respond to the words of wisdom you just shared with yourself?

_____

_____

_____

_____

_____

_____

_____

_____

Step Forward: You are that child in the exercise above. The child within you feels battered and bruised. How can you repair the relationship with your inner child and the skilled physician that you now are?

_____

_____

_____

_____

_____

_____

_____

_____

_____

To forgive ourselves for our limitations and failings takes time and practice. It helps to establish a ritual of self-forgiveness, such as ending each day with an assessment of all the things you accomplished, all the people you helped, and everything you learned. When you do so, the errors and failings seem less important. To the extent they linger, you can have a conversation with your inner child, based on what you wrote above.

Step Forward: How will a consistent ritual of self-forgiveness change your life and relationships with your patients?

_____

_____

_____

_____

_____

_____

_____

_____

_____

***

Not everything that is faced can be changed,
but nothing can be changed until it is faced.
James Baldwin

***

Seeking Hope

As more healthcare workers prepared to leave their jobs post-COVID-19, some predict we will lose up to three-quarters of the workforce. Many feel traumatized, anxious, and depressed, and some have seen shifts in their workload beyond their control. The workload for many physicians has increased, while for others, their workload has been reduced, and for still others, in the middle of a health crisis, they were fired. Given this critical state our profession now faces, it's important to not lose hope. Having hope for the future gives us meaning.

Contemplation: As a physician who wishes to continue to practice medicine, what does hope mean to you?

_____

_____

_____

_____

_____

_____

_____

Reflection: Do you know any physicians thriving in their profession and personal lives? Why do you think they are thriving? What can you learn from them?

_____

_____

_____

_____

_____

_____

_____

_____

Step Forward: When you think about regaining hope to continue practicing medicine, how can you restore power and autonomy over your practice of medicine?

_____

_____

_____

_____

_____

_____

_____

_____

Step Forward: What qualities in yourself do you feel you need to nurture more in order to create new possibilities in your life?

_____

_____

_____

_____

***

Hope is the thing with feathers that perches in the soul and sings the tunes without the words and never stops at all.

Emily Dickinson

***

Powerless to Powerful

At the beginning of this journal, you wrote about feeling powerless. There are so many ways in which we feel powerless as physicians, from being limited by the mandates of insurance companies, to being unable to persuade our patients to live healthier lives. Having reflected on all the ways you feel disempowered, now it's time to reflect on all the ways in which you feel you do have power in your life. Whether it's your inner strength, your capacity to love, heal and even save the lives of your patients, or your multitude of skills, there are a number of ways in which you have power in your life. That power might be professional power, economic power, or social power. It might also be an inner power that keeps you going or enables you to get back up when you collapse.

One way in which we can become and feel more empowered is through assertiveness. Women and people of color are particularly taught to hold back and not speak up for themselves. As physicians, we need to be able to stand up for what is right for ourselves and the patients we serve with confidence and a calm demeanor. Assertiveness is not passive or aggressive, it is communicating truthfully while respecting others. Assertiveness is a skill that will help reduce your sense of hopelessness, powerlessness, frustration, and anger when embraced. Assertiveness will reveal what is right for you and suitable for others. The tension can lead to you staying in a dysfunctional relationship or moving away from it so that you can live a life more true to yourself.

Step Forward: In what ways do you feel you could be more assertive in your personal and professional life? What needs do you need to feel, and to say, to communicate these needs in an assertive, but nonaggressive, manner?

_____

_____

_____

_____

_____

_____

_____

_____

_____

Step Forward: Assertiveness is closely tied to communicating what one needs. When our needs are not met and respected, our sense of being violated and unvalued can cause us to shut down, or to explode in anger. Think of something you want to tell someone in your professional or personal life about your needs that are not being met. How could you say it?

_____

_____

_____

_____

_____

_____

_____

_____

_____

Step Forward: Think about some of the ways you have power in your life. Brainstorm your professional, personal, social, and inner powers.

_____

_____

_____

_____

_____

_____

_____

_____

_____

Contemplation: Facing one adverse event after the other can create a dysregulated nervous system. People who have had more adverse events in their lives find it increasingly difficult when additional adversity strikes. But adversity also helps us to grow and develop new coping skills. Think about the adverse events and circumstances you have navigated in your career. How do you feel these misfortunes have helped you to grow and evolve?

_____

_____

_____

_____

_____

_____

_____

_____

Step Forward: What would it look like if you were to tap into those powers and engage them? How do you think you might be perceived by others? What might change in your life?

_____

_____

_____

_____

_____

_____

_____

_____

_____

_____

***

Strength is found in weakness. Control is found in dependency.
Power is found in surrender.
Dan B. Allender

Reinvent Yourself

As you come to the end of this journal, you may recognize changes in yourself, changes that may in some ways be confusing. Reflecting on the many ways we are wounded by our work can bring up difficult feelings. But just as any wound grows more sore before it begins to heal, so too do our emotions feel tender and sore as we heal from them. Healing requires tremendous energy, but the healing journey leads to radical change in how we interact with our work. By recognizing the abusive nature of our work, we become empowered to set boundaries and move toward more enriching relationships, more fulfilling work, and more clarity in our lives.

Contemplation: As you have been reflecting on your work as a physician, what changes have you noticed in yourself? How do you feel about these changes?

_____

_____

_____

_____

_____

_____

_____

_____

Healing requires making changes, but change can be difficult. Changing jobs means putting even more work into your day as you embark on the job search. It means risking rejection. It often means making another move—

which can entail getting your spouse on board, uprooting your kids from their school and friends, selling your home, and buying a new one. Changing perspective can be even more challenging—it means rethinking our beliefs about the world and ourselves. Ambivalence about these changes can freeze us, keeping us stuck in our wounds.

Contemplation: Think about ambivalence, are you stuck and unable to decide your next step and career? Are you still holding the tension of trying to serve two masters, your patients, and the healthcare system? In what ways do you feel ambivalent about change?

_____

_____

_____

_____

_____

_____

_____

Step Forward: In what ways do you feel confident about making changes in your life and work?

_____

_____

_____

_____

_____

_____

_____

_____

_____

Contemplation: What are the potential risks of not making any changes?

_____

_____

_____

_____

_____

_____

_____

_____

Contemplation: What are the potential rewards of making some changes?

_____

_____

_____

_____

_____

_____

_____

_____

Create! Can you draw and color a picture of the "new" physician you have become?

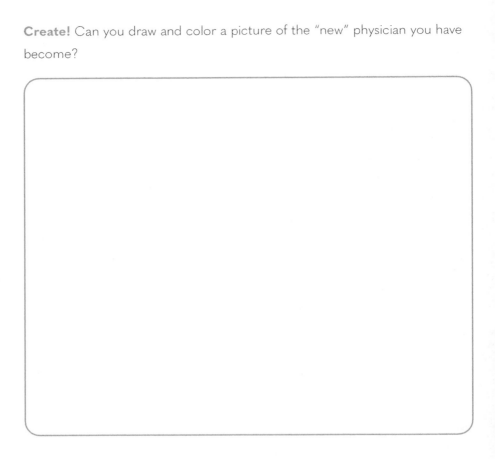

Trauma is not necessarily feeling traumatized. Trauma leads to changes in our bodies and our style of relating to ourselves, others, and the world. The debris of traumatic events can create an unseen cycle and storm. It is not until we stop and observe from a distance and with curiosity that we can see the damage. Trauma leaves us fragmented. We become broken into smaller parts that do not communicate or relate to each other. Our true identity and values are shattered into pieces. At times, all land in different places. Traumatic events lead to numbness. You might feel it is better not to feel at all than to feel pain too challenging to contain. When our trauma feels too big, shameful, or unique, we succumb to isolation. The secrecy and silence of isolation only augment the voice of those writing our stories, purpose, and future.

***

Reinvent yourself over and over and over and over and over until you find home. There is no timeline for the soul.

Malebo Sephardi

***

Contemplation: What is your biggest challenge in your healing journey right now?

_____

_____

_____

_____

_____

_____

_____

_____

_____

Step Forward: What can you do about it?

_____

_____

_____

_____

_____

_____

_____

_____

From Weakness Comes Our Strength

Our emotional backpacks become heavier as we carry the wounds from medical training, patients' disrespect, and unreal expectations. Something that can help us build resiliency for hard times are our unique character strengths. Developing and using our individual strengths can help us live in our window of tolerance and thus feel safe and relate better with others. The window of tolerance is where you can listen and learn, respond, and manage the daily stress and challenges as they arise.

Despite our many strengths, it is common to focus on our weaknesses, thinking that our weaknesses override or limit our strengths in some ways. Yet our weaknesses can be transformed into strengths. For example, dyslexics have difficulty reading, so many learn "work arounds" that help them to compensate for their reading challenges, and these work arounds become not just adaptations, but strengths—such as skills in problem-solving, making sense of fragments of information, and superior study skills. In my own education, because English is my second language, writing in English is not easy. Consequently, I've not only found tools to improve my English skills (such as working with Grammarly software), but I've focused more on public speaking and oral presentations than writing. As a result, I'm a seasoned public speaker, skilled in making professional presentations that engage an audience, and have frequent requests to teach and provide presentations to staff and colleagues on a variety of topics. Had I been more comfortable writing, I might still be hiding behind a keyboard afraid to step in front of an audience!

Character strengths are another example of how our weaknesses can be transformed into strengths. Character strengths are those personal abilities and skills that in the past have helped you overcome difficult times and have helped you get out of challenging situations. Strengths can also be the skills and abilities that helped you reach your goals in the past. Using these strengths daily will help you to achieve more at work with less energy requirement—and give you a sense of safety as you become more confident in your strengths.

Step Forward: List five traits or habits you consider to be your weaknesses. For each one, reflect on how you can compensate for that "weakness" in some way.

_____

_____

_____

_____

_____

_____

_____

_____

_____

Step Forward: What are your top 5 strengths?
For each one, reflect on how you can use that strength in your physician-patient relationships.

_____

_____

_____

_____

_____

_____

_____

_____

_____

_____

Step Forward: In what ways can you use these strengths to achieve a sense of inner and outer calmness that creates a daily rhythm of harmony between your external and internal worlds? Be creative in your answers. Allow yourself to imagine your strengths having the power to change your world.

_____

_____

_____

_____

_____

_____

_____

_____

***

The world breaks everyone, and afterward many are
strong in the broken places.
Ernest Hemingway, A Farewell to Arms

***

Final Reflections

The journey of healing has been long. We have many tasks daily, and you did the courageous work of examination and introspection with curiosity and openness. Well done! I hope you have been able to embrace the beauty and redeem the harm of your chosen profession. Ours is a profession devoted to the care and healing of others, and for that we are proud. Let us be as proud of our own care and healing as we go forward.

As you come to our final pages, you've written about so many pains and joys and dreams and frustrations in your work and life. You've also discovered new ways to heal and gain a sense of power and autonomy in your life. Being a doctor does not have to mean living a life of constant stress and anxiety. You've attained so much in life—you deserve to reward yourself and acknowledge your achievements. The tangible and risky or courageous changes you have made will start making their way into your everyday life as you come to live in harmony internally and externally.

No one can live a life free of struggles. But as you think about the struggles of the past, think, as well, about the gifts of today and the presents of tomorrow. As we bring these pages to a close, I want you to become aware of your own transformation. Let's give some final thought to how you can tap into the changes and growth you've discovered through your writing journey.

Contemplation: What are some of the personal gifts that have come from your brokenness that others perhaps cannot see, but are alive in the care you give to your patients?

_____

_____

_____

_____

_____

_____

_____

_____

Reflection: What do you do when a patient says thank you? How do you feel? Do you say or think, well it is my job? Or can you honestly receive their appreciation for your calling as an acknowledgment of your worth?

_____

_____

_____

_____

_____

_____

Step Forward: Medicine and life should be fun and not a burden. Think about some of the ways you have released this burden through your journaling. What can you do to not pick up that burden again, or to drop that shitty weight when it becomes too much to bear?

_____

_____

_____

_____

_____

_____

_____

_____

_____

_____

Step Forward: As you've worked through this journal, you'll have discovered that you can't "fix" the broken parts of your life, but you can restore them, creating beauty and life again where you once felt hopeless. Think about some of the ways you've regained your agency and authorship not only over your life but also in the way you practice medicine. In what ways do you feel revitalized and stronger?

_____

_____

_____

_____

_____

_____

_____

_____

_____

Before closing your journal, let's take some time to rethink the journey you've been on. Use this time and space to reconsider the ways in which you can acknowledge your capacities and embrace your incapacities.

Reflection: Where have you come from and where are you going? How has medicine impacted your life journey?

_____

_____

_____

_____

_____

_____

_____

_____

Contemplation: What do you need to honor and what lessons are you taking with you? What have you decided to leave behind because it does not serve any purpose now?

_____

_____

_____

_____

_____

_____

_____

Step Forward: What new narratives do you need for yourself in order to continue to create and express your true self?

_____

_____

_____

_____

_____

_____

_____

_____

_____

_____

Contemplation: What self-contempt, self-hatred, or shame are you releasing today? How do you feel as you release these feelings?

_____

_____

_____

_____

_____

_____

_____

_____

Step Forward: What new lens have you gained as you've done these exercises, and in what ways does this new lens help you feel more whole?

_____

_____

_____

_____

_____

_____

Contemplation: In what ways do you feel empowered in your life?

Step Forward: How can you accept and embrace the areas in your life where you have no power?

Contemplation: What do you feel you have surrendered in your life?

_____

_____

_____

_____

_____

_____

_____

Step Forward: How can you surrender to those elements in your life that are beyond your control, power, or strength? In what ways does giving up not mean giving in, but growing into a new, more vibrant you?

_____

_____

_____

_____

_____

_____

_____

_____

_____

Contemplation: What new interpretations of the events in your life, and in those of your patients, have helped you to provide better care to your patients?

_____

_____

_____

_____

_____

_____

_____

_____

Reflection: After completing the exercises in this journal, how hard has it been to accept the truth of the effects of trauma due to your profession?

_____

_____

_____

_____

_____

_____

_____

_____

As you continue in your life and career, the stress and anxiety will return, along with the sense of being overwhelmed, ashamed, "less than," or whatever it is that knocks you back down. Fortunately, breathing does not require any work at all. We breathe effortlessly, as we sustain our lives. Return to the breath work exercises any time you need to ground yourself and restore your energy. It takes only minutes to make a radical shift in your energy and outlook.

Finally, I want to leave you with an exercise to help you develop your own manifesto or rule of life. Pick up your pen once again and identify the three principles in life that are most important to you.

No matter what, I will lead my life and carry out my work by these three guiding principles:

_____

_____

_____.

_____

_____

_____.

_____

_____

_____.

***

We begin to discern new paths that are body guided. We start to live in rhythms and cycles that are nourishing rather than depleting. We touch a primal joy that is our birthright.
Christine Valters Painter

***

As we draw to our close in this journaling journey, I invite you to continue journaling and engaging in narrative practices. Consider some contemplations and reflections of your own, and take your own, unique, steps forward as you grow into the person and the doctor you were meant to be. Journaling and writing will help you to let go of your traumas, as no human, and no doctor is trained to be a superhero. You were not created to carry the weight of pain and the suffering of all humanity on your shoulders. Journaling is an essential component of your self-care, a gift you give yourself regardless of the time or energy demands upon you. You are worthy of the time and space to chart your own journey and give words and stories to the emotions you feel as a doctor, a human, and an essential element in this vast universe to which we are all connected.

Notes

Resources

The following list of resources should help you whenever you feel you need help quickly or want to dive into one of the topics we've covered to learn more.

Books

1. *The Body Keeps the Score: Brain, Mind, and Body in the Healing of Trauma* by Bessel van der Kolk M.D. Penguin Publishing, 2015.
2. *When the Body Says No* by Gabor Maté M.D. Wiley Publishers, 2011.
3. *Try Softer: A Fresh Approach to Move Us out of Anxiety, Stress, and Survival Mode--and into a Life of Connection and Joy* by **Aundi Kolber**, Tyndale Refresh, 2020 (book and workbook).
4. *To Be Told: God Invites You to Coauthor Your Future* by Dan B. Allender, Waterbrook, 2009 (book and workbook).
5. *The EntreMD Method: A Proven Roadmap for Doctors Who Want to Live Life and Practice Medicine on Their Terms* by **Nneka Unachukwu, EntreMD Publishing, 2022.**
6. *Doc-Related: A Physician's Guide to Fixing Our Ailing Health Care System* by Peter Valenzuela, Lucere Leadership 2021.
7. *Managing Transitions (25th Anniversary Edition): Making Sense of Life's Changes* by **William Bridges** and **Susan Bridges, DeCapo Lifelong Books, 2017.**
8. *The Comfort Crisis: Embrace Discomfort to Reclaim Your Wild, Happy, Healthy Self* by **Michael Easter, Rodale Books, 2021.**
9. *Life Is in the Transitions: Mastering Change at Any Age* by Bruce Feiler, Penguin Books, 2021.
10. *Hero Within: Six Archetypes We Live By, Revised and Expanded Edition* by **Carol Pearson, Harper One, 2013.**

11. *Loving What Is, Revised Edition: Four Questions That Can Change Your Life* by **Byron Katie, Harmony, 2021.**
12. If you want to have some coloring books, my favorite coloring books for doctors can be found on Amazon: https://www.amazon.com/Doctor-LifeA-Snarky-Adult-Coloring-Book/dp/1640010742

Poetry

Explore the poetry of David Whyte and Morgan Harper Nichols for inspiration and comfort.

Podcasts

I have found the following podcasts to be great sources of inspiration and information:
1. The EntreMD
2. CEO Blind Spots
3. Carpe diem
4. Doctors Changing Medicine
5. Talk2MeDoc
6. Moral Matters

Coaching

Coaching can be an excellent way to feel supported and encouraged. Here are some I recommend:
1. https://www.instituteforphysicianwellness.com
2. https://www.thehappymd.com/
3. https://drernestomd.com/

TED Talks

1. *Good Relationships Are the Key to Healing Trauma* by Dr. Karen Treismen
2. *What Trauma Taught Me About Resilience* by Charles Hunt
3. *Understanding PTSD's Effects on Brain, Body, and Emotions* by Janet

Seahorn

4. *Why You Should Define Your Fears Instead of Your Goals* by Tim Ferriss

5. *Anger Is Your Ally: A Mindful Approach to Anger* by Juan Mustad

Other self-care tools to attend to the body

1. Teas—create a ritual of making and serving tea using the finest teas and beautiful teacups to treat yourself each afternoon

2. A weighted blanket (blankets filled with small weights that conform to your body)

3. Essential oils

4. Candles

5. Spa days (either at home or professionally)

6. Soothing music, whether classical, folk, spiritual, or whatever you love that calms your soul

Others

Anticipate Joy is a mental health company that provides services to healthcare professionals. If you find you need additional help, contact them: https://anticipatejoy.com/

If you feel your complete health is in danger because medicine has not allowed you to practice wellness and self-care, this quiz will help you discover the area where changes can start to happen. https://wheelofwellbeing.com/quiz/

Want to learn more about your personal strengths and abilities? VIA Character, https:// www.viacharacter.org, provides a free 15-minute assessment, description, and tips on using your strengths to live more fully. If you need and want to explore your values, I recommend using this online tool with a free assessment and explaining each universal importance: https://personalvalu.es/.

Acknowledgements

It wouldn't have been possible to write this journal without the many people who have inspired and supported me throughout my medical career. They have been here from the beginning and in one way or another they continue to be present in my life. They include:

Ricardo González Santoni MD, the first family doctor I knew. By taking care of me and my family he has continued to inspire me. Thank you for the endless support during medical school.

John Sheffield MD, who believed in me and saw beyond the Puerto Rican women. Your love and dedication for teaching led me into academia and your support during residency kept me going. I still love working with trainees and leading them into family medicine.

Fadya El Rayess MD MPH, gave me an opportunity up North and abroad. Thank you for your kindness in the midst of such hard work, and for teaching me the importance of mentorship and introducing me to others.

Gowri Anandarajah MD, thank you for your patience and non-judgment. Writing for academic journals is challenging for this Puerto Rican doctor, but you saw beyond that.

Maria Munoz MD, we will always be team M&M. Thank you for the friendship in the midst of the chaos (and the chocolate M&Ms), and for the shared laughs and love for medical students.

Shannon Murphy MD, thank you for 10 plus years of friendship and support in this life and in our medical careers. We have panicked together and also gotten out if it together.

Tio Charlie, Carlos Mendez-Bryan MD, thank you for all the little monthly checks that helped me pay for school, reduce my debt, and quit my part-time job while in medical school. And thank you for taking me out during med school to just have fun in front of the beach.

Finally, thank you Abueli, Carmen Mendez-Bryan, for taking me to buy my first stethoscope. I still have it and carry it with me every day when I see my patients. Your love for medicine has followed me each day throughout my career.

Author

Dr. Maria is native to Puerto Rico. She completed medical school at the University of Puerto Rico Science Medical Campus. Her postgraduate training included the Penn State University Family & Community Medicine Residency Program and Faculty Development for Global Health fellowship at Warren Alpert School of Medicine. After a long journey of self-discovery and self-healing, she decided to blend her passions with medicine. She is a Family & Lifestyle Medicine physician with a holistic approach to serving the Hispanic and

LatinX communities. She is a fellow of the Academy of Integrative Health & Medicine. She has added to her breath of knowledge nutrition via the T Colin Campbell Center for Nutritional Studies, yoga via YogaFaith, and embodiment via the HearthMath technique. Nature is her monastery. She lives in Texas in a small home with her husband, Jason Alan Raleigh, and her furry babies Scooby, Venus, and Mercy.

Made in the USA
Monee, IL
18 June 2023

35608976R00122